Cartoon Corner

MW00388958

Cartoon Corner

Humor-Based Mathematics Activities

A Collection Adapted from "Cartoon Corner" in
Mathematics Teaching in the Middle School

Edited by
Andy Reeves
University of South Florida St. Petersburg

NCTM
NATIONAL COUNCIL OF
TEACHERS OF MATHEMATICS

1906 Association Drive, Reston, VA 20191-1502
(703) 620-9840; (800) 235-7566; www.nctm.org

Second Printing 2009

Library of Congress Cataloging-in-Publication Data

Cartoon corner : humor-based mathematics activities : a collection adapted from "Cartoon Corner" in mathematics teaching in the middle school / edited by Andy Reeves.
p. cm.
ISBN 978-0-87353-600-4
1. Mathematics—Study and teaching (Middle school)—United States. 2. Mathematics—Study and teaching (Middle school)—Activity programs. 3. Mathematics—Humor I. Reeves, Andy.
QA135.6.C42 2007
510.71'2—dc22
2007016942

The National Council of Teachers of Mathematics is a public voice of mathematics education, providing vision, leadership, and professional development to support teachers in ensuring mathematics learning of the highest quality for all students.

Printed in the United States of America

Contents

History of *Cartoon Corner: Humor-Based Mathematics Activities*

The founding Editorial Panel of the journal *Mathematics Teaching in the Middle School (MTMS)* consisted of Jay Greenwood (Chair), James V. Bruni, Pamela Giles, Kay J. McClain, Beatrice Moore Harris, Linda L. Walker, and Earlene Hemmer. Working in consort with the Publications Division of the National Council of Teachers of Mathematics (NCTM), directed by Harry Tunis, the founding Editorial Panel members put many ideas on the table for discussion over several years. A primary concern was that the journal offer practical ideas and useful resources for teachers in the middle grades. One idea that surfaced was that cartoons closely connected with the classroom might make a unique contribution. The "Cartoon Corner" department was off and running, with Barbara Cain as its first editor, and made its initial appearance in the premier issue, April 1994.

Barbara set the standard for the department. She had used cartoons in her own classroom for many years and was an ideal fit for the editorship of "Cartoon Corner" with *MTMS* in its fledgling stages. Barbara served as the department's editor from 1994 to 1995. A succession of editors followed Barbara, each contributing her or his unique ideas and perspectives. Ann Lawrence, Julie Fisher, Judith A. (Judy) White, Kris Warloe, and Sue McMillen each took a turn editing this popular department of *MTMS*. The "Cartoon Corner" editors at the time this book was being prepared were Andy Reeves, a mathematics educator from University of South Florida St. Petersburg, and Mary Lou Beasley, a mathematics coach and classroom teacher with Pinellas County Schools in St. Petersburg, Florida.

I was asked by NCTM's Educational Materials Committee to put together a collection of past issues of "Cartoon Corner" and, if possible, to make them even more teacher friendly. Mary Lou Beasley and I first selected cartoons under topics most likely to be used in the classroom, then arranged them so that a teacher could photocopy a cartoon and its related questions as a single page. We asked previous editors to join us, and two were able to do so—Sue McMillen and Judy White. We also tested these materials with practicing classroom teachers and used their feedback to improve the activity sheets.

This book is therefore a refinement of the past efforts of many mathematics educators. It would not have been possible without the hard work of the previous editors, the Editorial Panel liaisons for "Cartoon Corner," and the NCTM Headquarters Office staff. I and the contributing editors are glad to offer our own perspectives and do so humbly. We realize that if not "standing on the shoulders of giants," we are at least "standing on the shoulders of some very tall people."

Andy Reeves, *Editor*

Acknowledgments

The editor wishes to give special recognition to the following individuals for their significant contributions to the success of this volume:

Contributing Editors
Mary Lou Beasley
Kaplan K12 Learning Services
Largo, Florida

Sue McMillen
Buffalo State College
Buffalo, New York

Judith A. White (retired)
Parker Middle School
Chelmsford, Massachusetts

As previous editors of "Cartoon Corner," they not only provided substantive material to form the core of this publication but also updated and revised their previous work to fit the style of this volume. Additionally, they worked with classroom teachers in their districts to field-test the cartoon-related activities they had prepared. Mary Lou Beasley headed up field testing in the Pinellas County, Florida, public schools; Sue McMillen worked with teachers in Buffalo, New York.

Former "Cartoon Corner" editors Barbara Cain, Ann Lawrence, Julie Fisher, and Kris Warloe also deserve a special thank-you for providing high-quality material that was easy to modify for the new format of this book.

The teachers who field-tested these activities with their students deserve special thanks for contributing their expertise to make this product useful for other teachers. The teachers who worked with contributing editor Mary Lou Beasley in Pinellas County, Florida, were Peggy Bodine, Barbara Brown, Yvette De Rollo, Greg Fanning, Jeanne Gagliardo, Rhody Gecan, Mary Jackson, Bennie Royal Smith, Joyce Wiley, and Elizabeth Wright. The teachers who worked with contributing editor Sue McMillen in Buffalo, New York, were Harmonie Conte, Caitlin Ianonne, Kristen Lasker, and Stephanie Saviola.

Additionally, classroom teachers were recruited from across the United States through an advertisement in *Mathematics Teaching in the Middle School* to field-test the cartoon activities with their classes. The following teachers were invaluable in reporting the results of their students' experiences with the activities in a timely fashion, enabling the publication to proceed on time: Kristin Dailey, Kevin Dykema, Susan Eith, Anita Finn, Gail Englert, Pam Gretton, Ellen Horlick, David Johnston,

Glenn Kenyon, Tom Lewis, Lynn Prichard, Emmie Treadwell, Kristen Weller, and Sue Younker.

The NCTM staff warrant a special accolade for contributing encouragement and insight during the project. Harry Tunis, Dolores Pesek, Nancy Busse, Patrick Vennebush, and Ann Butterfield all made significant contributions in time and expertise.

This book is truly a collaborative effort of many people.

Andy Reeves, *Editor*

1

Ways to Use Cartoons in the Classroom

USING CARTOONS on a regular basis can enliven the mathematics classroom in many ways. We invite you to think along with us about using the contents of this book in a creative manner. Some of the ways discussed in the following paragraphs may be obvious to you, but you might get a new idea by reading further.

Preparation and Organization

A note about the technical aspects of using this collection of cartoons is in order. First, field tests demonstrated the desirability of discussing the cartoon itself with students, as the humor is often rather subtle to mathematically unsophisticated readers. Second, these pages are designed for you to copy the first page with the cartoon and questions, leaving the reverse of the sheet blank for students who need more room to write than is provided with the questions. Occasionally the directions tell students to record an answer on the back of the page. And third, the cartoons are loosely grouped in the contents list by primary topic, but many of them overlap several topics.

Suggested Uses for Cartoons

Introducing a topic. Introducing or re-introducing a mathematics topic is one primary use of cartoons. To re-introduce the topic of prime numbers, for example, you might use a cartoon such as "Don't Ride with Loon!" The cartoon activity sheet shows a different approach to prime numbers than the traditional one of making various rectangles, given a certain number of tiles, which is often used in the elementary grades.

Preassessment. Cartoon activity sheets can often be used as a preassessment of what students know about a topic. "A Square by Any Other Name," for example, might serve as a preassessment of what students know about polygons before starting a geometry unit.

Wrap up. Wrapping up a unit is also an appropriate use of cartoons. A cartoon such as "Reciprocal Agreement" can be used after students have studied reciprocals. The cartoon might show students a different way to think about or remember the topic they have just studied. Several teachers have found that some cartoons in this collection could be used both to introduce a topic and to wrap it up—see the field-test comments for "Rainman" as an example.

Group work. Using cartoons might offer an interesting way for your assessment system to align with the way you conduct class. For example, if students work together in small groups during class, then a portion of an examination might logically involve a group effort. Accordingly, a cartoon might be included as a take-home portion of a chapter examination, given out a few days before the test. Students could work together in groups to respond to the cartoon's questions, and the entire group would receive the same grade on the corresponding portion of the examination.

Extra credit. Students or their parents often request extra-credit assignments, and a cartoon with ready-made questions might provide that resource. In such instances, you want the assignments you give to be beneficial for the students but not a substitute for regular class work. The activities included in this book might provide such an opportunity.

Shortened class period. A planned shortened school day or class period—perhaps shortened because of a schoolwide assembly, a teacher planning day, or the like—offers another possible use for cartoons. You might keep your classes on the same pace by using a cartoon as an enrichment activity for one class on a day that another class does not meet.

Holiday activity. Prior to a holiday, when students are excited and likely not attentive to a regular lesson, cartoons might again be used successfully. The cartoons in the section labeled "Holidays" in the Contents provide the opportunity for that possibility.

Parents' night. Cartoons might be useful for a parents' night presentation. If you have such an occasion, a cartoon might allow you to "talk serious mathematics" in a light-hearted way, thus putting the parents at ease and giving you a chance to subtly win over their support. An activity such as

"Cool Beans" might also offer the opportunity for parents and students to work together on a homework assignment.

Review for state assessment. These cartoons might also be used as a spiraling review for state assessments. Many of the cartoons have discussion questions that incorporate multiple concepts and allow students distributive practice on topics they are not currently studying in mathematics class. The teacher could assign all the questions, if appropriate, or only the questions for which the class has already studied the material. See "Loud, Louder, Loudest" as an example of an interesting way to review sales tax and percent increase and decrease prior to a high-stakes test.

Mathematics club resource. Still another use for a collection of cartoons is as a resource for a school mathematics club. Students might also identify other mathematics-related cartoons, formulate questions, and provide solutions, exchanging cartoons with other students when they have finished their own.

Student cartooning. Yet another idea is to have students modify or create their own cartoons related to a mathematics topic. "Creativity: A Key to Understanding" (Lynch 1997) and "Balloons on the Rise: A Problem-Solving Introduction to Integers" (Reeves and Webb 2004) might give you ideas for how to begin cartooning in your classroom.

Sharing Your Ideas

If you enjoy using the cartoon activities in this book, then be sure to join NCTM and subscribe to *Mathematics Teaching in the Middle School.* Ready-to-use activities like those in this book are a regular feature of that journal. If you have other ways in which you have used cartoons, please suggest them to your fellow teachers in a letter to *Mathematics Teaching in the Middle School.* Write to "Readers Write," MTMS, 1906 Association Drive, Reston, VA 20191. The Editorial Panel of the journal would like to hear from you.

References

Lynch, Diane. "Creativity: A Key to Understanding." *Mathematics Teaching in the Middle School* 2 (March–April 1997): 350–51.

Reeves, Charles A. (Andy), and Darcy Webb. "Balloons on the Rise: A Problem-Solving Introduction to Integers." *Mathematics Teaching in the Middle School* 9 (May 2004): 476–82.

2
Algebraic Thinking

A Sheepish Problem

1. If n is equal to 200, what is the value of $n - 1$ and $n + 1$?

2. Suppose that n is an even number; how would you represent the next even number greater than n? The previous even number less than n?

3. Write a mathematical sentence that could be used to determine the value of n if the sum of the three numbers in the cartoon is 159. What are the three numbers? Show your work below.

4. This mathematician usually counts to at least 3000 before falling asleep. At the rate of one number per second, about how long would it take him to fall asleep? Show your work below.

5. **Challenge:** Pretend that the sheep are all lined up waiting to be counted. Billy the Bully sheep doesn't want to wait his turn. He's 46th in line to start, but every time a sheep is counted, Billy jumps ahead of 2 sheep. How many sheep will be counted before Billy? Draw a picture to help you decide.

Solutions

1. $n - 1 = 200 - 1 = 199$; $n + 1 = 200 + 1 = 201$.
2. The next even number after n would be $n + 2$. The previous even number less than n would be $n - 2$.
3. The number sentence is $(n - 1) + n + (n + 1) = 159$. Students can solve for n in several ways. They might use the *guess-check-revise* technique. Or knowing that three numbers are involved, they might divide 159 by 3 to get n, then add and subtract 1 to get the other two numbers. Or they might solve $(n - 1) + n + (n + 1) = 159$ by collecting like terms and simplifying the equation to $3n = 159$. Then they would divide both sides by 3 and have $n = 53$. So $n - 1$ and $n + 1$ are 52 and 54, respectively.
4. Students can divide 3000 seconds by 60 seconds per minute and get 50 minutes that the mathematician takes to fall asleep.
5. Students will enjoy using manipulatives, acting this problem out, or drawing a diagram to solve it. Fifteen sheep will be counted before Billy.

Field-Test Comments

I used this activity in mid-November as a warm-up for my 8th-grade algebra class. I sometimes use cartoons as icebreakers, so they took immediately to the format. The problems were all accessible to the students, with teacher direction.

Jeanne Gagliardo
Safety Harbor Middle School
Safety Harbor, Florida

This activity was used in prealgebra and Algebra I honors classes in October at Southside Fundamental Middle School in St. Petersburg, Florida. Changes were made in the activity on the basis of the teacher's verbal comments. The Algebra I honors students found the worksheet easy and enjoyable, and the teacher thought it was also good preparation for the prealgebra students' later work.

Andy Reeves
University of South Florida–St. Petersburg
St. Petersburg, Florida

Other Ideas

- Problem 5 is similar to *Eric the Sheep* from the Annenberg/CPB professional development video series titled Learning Math: Patterns, Functions, and Algebra. For more on this series, visit www.learner.org. The problem can be altered by having Billy start at a different place in line, or take different-sized jumps each time.
- As another option, ask students what the labels on the sheep would read if the mathematician counted by 2s, by 3s, and so forth.

Adapted from "Cartoon Corner," *Mathematics Teaching in the Middle School,* January–March 1995, page 300, edited by Barbara Cain

Back Scratchin'

Arlo & Janis *by Johnson*

Arlo and Janis, by Johnson, 12/14/99. © Newspaper Enterprise Association, Inc.

1. Arlo wants Janis to follow these directions: Go to the left 3 inches and then up 2 inches. How do we usually write this instruction as an ordered pair for graphing?

2. How would you give the verbal instructions for the ordered pair (4, –3)?

3. If Arlo's right shoulder itched, what quadrant would Janis scratch? _____ If Arlo had an itch in his lower-left back, what's a point he might tell Janis to scratch? Write it as an ordered pair. _______

4. Work with a partner. Each person should take two strips of masking tape about 16 inches long and mark them in1-inch increments. Place an axis system on the back of both shirts as shown below. Have your partner put a finger on (0, 0) so you can feel it. Then have them use a finger to trace a 4-by-6 rectangle, stopping at each vertex. They can tell you the length of the line but not its direction. Try to name each vertex using coordinates. Then you and your partner swap roles. Describe below how successful you were and anything you learned.

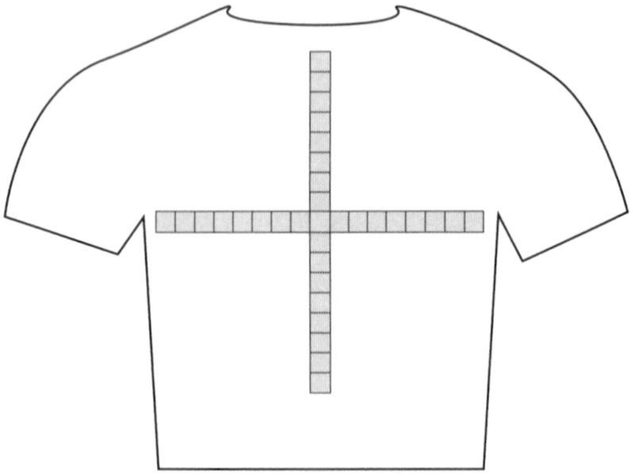

Solutions

1. (–3, 2)
2. Go to the right 4 inches and then down 3 inches.
3. Quadrant I. One such point in the lower left is (–6, –5). Any two negative numbers would be acceptable coordinates.
4. Students will probably realize that spatial sense is required for them to visualize the coordinates, as they will be feeling them from the back of the grid rather than the front. If done in class, this activity might produce some laughter.

Field-Test Comments

I used this assignment with my five classes of 7th-grade advanced math students for a "shortened school day" in October. We had covered the coordinate plane prior to this class. I introduced the cartoon and the first three questions to the students individually. I then paired the students up to answer question 4. Marking inches on the masking tape before putting it on the students' back[s] would probably save time and be easier. This worksheet offered an excellent extension to the coordinate plane lessons. The students enjoyed the experiment, and many wanted to wear the masking tape around all day to tell other students about their classroom project.

Yvette DeRollo
Southside Fundamental Middle School
St. Petersburg, Florida

Other Ideas

- Have students look at the shirt shown in problem 4 and do problems like these:

  (a) For someone to rub the back of your neck, what coordinates would you tell them to use?

  (b) Put your left arm behind your back and your right arm over your right shoulder, and touch your hands. In what quadrant are you? Reverse the arms, and where are you?

  (c) Put your hands on your hips. Give the coordinates of both thumbs.

  (d) Name two points that would determine a line parallel to your belt, or your waist. Name two points that would determine a line parallel to your backbone but moved left 6 inches. Name three points that would make an equilateral triangle with the right angle in quadrant IV. With advanced students, you could ask them to name two points on a line with slope –5, and so forth.

- For a graphing activity in which students draw pictures in the coordinate plane, visit NCTM's Illuminations Web site at http://illuminations.nctm.org/LessonDetail.aspx?id=L280.

Adapted from "Cartoon Corner," *Mathematics Teaching in the Middle School,* January 2001, page 307, edited by Judith A. White

Love That Pizza!

Garfield *by Jim Davis*

Garfield loves Fausto's pizza! On the 1st day, he ate 5 pieces of pizza. On the 2nd day, he ate 8 pieces; and on the 3rd day, he ate 11 pieces. On each successive day, he ate 3 more pieces of pizza than on the previous day.

1. How many pieces of pizza did Garfield eat on the 10th day? Complete the chart to get the answer.

Day (n)	1	2	3	4	5	6	7	8	9	10
Pizza pieces (p)	5	8	11							

2. Find a mathematical rule that relates the number of the day (n) and the number of pieces of pizza (p) that Garfield ate that day. On what day did he eat exactly 200 pieces of pizza?

3. What is the total number of pieces of pizza Garfield ate in 10 days?

4. **Challenge:** Garfield orders his megacheese pizza with none, one, two, or three different toppings. In how many different ways can he order his pizza?

Solutions

1. Continue the sequence using the rule *add 3:* 5, 8, 11, 14, 17, 20, 23, 26, 29, 32. The 10th number in the sequence is 32.
2. Garfield ate 200 pieces on the 66th day. The rule is this: 3 times the number (n) of the day increased by 2 is equal to the number of pieces (p) of pizza eaten that day, or $3n + 2 = p$. Substitute 200 for p to get $3n + 2 = 200$. Solve to get $n = 66$.
3. Garfield ate 185 pieces of pizza in 10 days.
4. Garfield can order eight different pizzas: plain, onion, anchovy, pepperoni, onion-pepperoni, onion-anchovy, anchovy-pepperoni, everything. For a challenge, have students consider the number of combinations if double toppings of a particular type are allowed.

Field-Test Comments

I used this worksheet in mid-November with my regular 7th-grade classes using cooperative groups. Each student group had one low-, two medium-, and one high-achieving student so I could observe the interaction among the higher- and lower-performing students.

The difficulty levels of the questions varied on the worksheet—all of my students felt confident after solving the first problem, and they were more willing to begin the second, more challenging, problem. The student groups chose their own method of solving the second problem, and many of them used a graphic organizer to aid in finding the pattern. Most of my higher-level students could determine the rule without much difficulty, and they took time to explain their thinking to the others in their group. The third question was easier than the previous problem and so boosted everyone's confidence. The fourth question was interesting, as many of the higher-level students just wanted to use their background knowledge of combinations to solve it. A few of the lower-level students took time to use graphic organizers again, and they were able to "see" the different pizzas that could be made—they were ecstatic at being able to explain their thinking to the others in their group instead of being the ones listening to others' explanations.

I would recommend that other teachers use heterogeneous groups to obtain powerful group conversations, and that students be encouraged to use graphic organizers.

Kristin M. Weller
P. K. Yonge Developmental Research School
Gainesville, Florida

Other Ideas

- Use a coordinate graph with horizontal axis n, vertical axis p, and the equation $p = 3n + 2$ to illustrate the linear relationship between n and p.
- Have students check a local pizza shop to find the number of toppings it offers. How many one-, two-, or three-different-topping pizzas could Garfield order from your local pizza shop?
- Other patterning activities can be found at NCTM's Illuminations Web site. Consider two problems found at http://illuminations.nctm.org/LessonDetail.aspx?id=L286 and http://illuminations.nctm.org/LessonDetail.aspx?id=L627.

Adapted from "Cartoon Corner," *Mathematics Teaching in the Middle School,* April 2000, page 516, edited by Judith A. White

Why Weight?

FOXTROT BILL AMEND

1. Fill in the values in the table.

x	x^2
−2	
−1	
−0.5	
0	
0.5	
1	
2	

2. Make a graph from the values in your table. Plot 7 points using x for the x-coordinate and x^2 for the y-coordinate. Add points in the table for $x = 1.5$ and for $x = -1.5$. Check your graph by entering $y = x^2$ on a graphing calculator. The graph of $y = x^2$ is called a parabola.

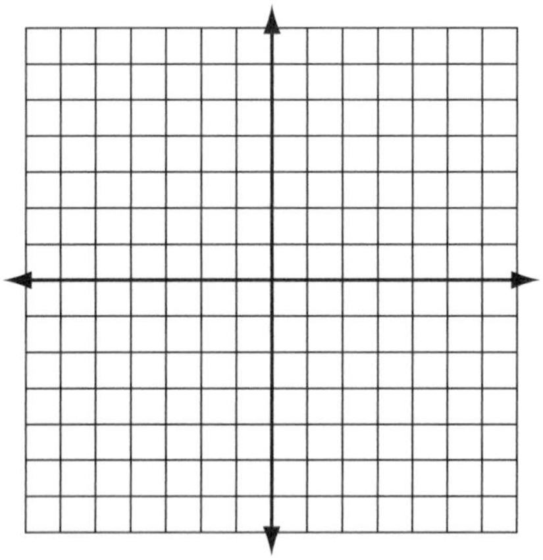

3. Use a graphing calculator to graph $y = x^2 + 2$ and $y = x^2 + 7$. On the back of this sheet, sketch and then predict what the graph of $y = x^2 + 5$ will look like. Check it on the graphing calculator.

4. Predict an equation that will produce the graph to the right, and check it on a graphing calculator.

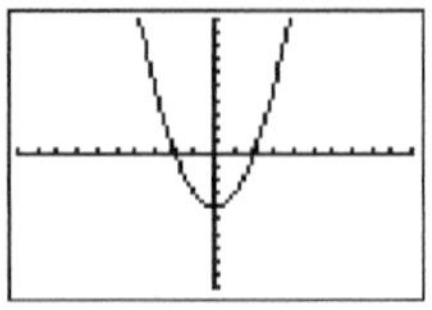

Prediction: ____________________

Equation: ____________________

5. Which of the parabolas below best models Jason's actions in the cartoon? Explain your reasoning.

$y = -x^2$

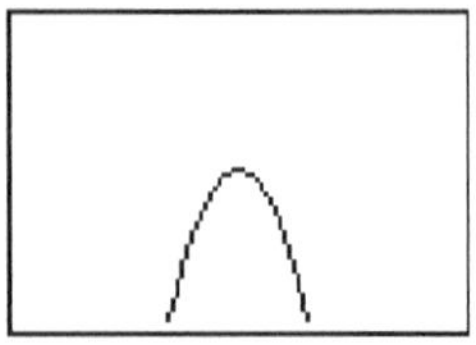

$y = -0.5x^2$

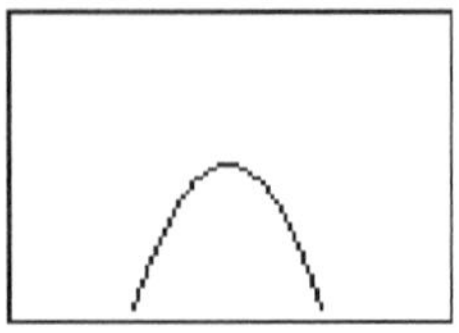

$y = -0.05x^2$

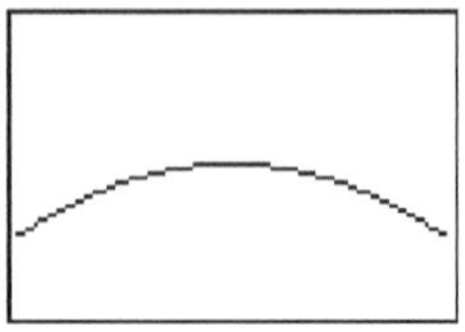

Solutions

1.

x	−2	−1	−0.5	0	0.5	1	2
x^2	4	1	0.25	0	0.25	1	4

4. $y = x^2 - 4$.
5. $y = -0.05x^2$; explanations will vary.

Field-Test Comments

My eighth grade, regular Algebra I class completed this worksheet following a unit on linear equations and functions. The students were all familiar with parabolas, as I had introduced them when we were graphing functions. Their familiarity proved quite helpful, as they immediately recognized what a parabola should look like and the correlation with the cartoon. I always like to make sure that students are able to draw the graphs by hand so that they can see the changes take place. As we learn what each basic function looks like, we first "discover" the function by taking a basic linear equation and manipulating the data. The data manipulation allows for students to see that seemingly small changes produce large results. The recognition that my class had, in my opinion, can be attributed to their experimentation with graphing. The worksheet was a fabulous extension because they were then able to make connections with what changes take place to create different parabolas.

My class generally sits in clusters, and I encourage children to help each other when questions arise. I was amazed to hear the depth of understanding that was exhibited as I listened to students explain their thoughts to others. Questions 3 and 4 allow for just enough repetition that almost all students are able to find connections, and therefore deepen their understanding of graphing and parabolas in general. Overall, I think that the worksheet was a successful extension of the material covered in basic Algebra I classes.

Emmie Treadwell
The Baylor School
Chattanooga, Tennessee

Other Ideas

- Start with the graph of $y = x^2$, and challenge students with various transformation tasks, for example:
    - Write an equation that will create each transformation. Check your equation on your graphing calculator.
        - Move the graph 5 units to the right.
        - Move the graph 2 units left and 3.5 units up.
- Give students the coordinates of two points, for example, (1, 3) and (2, −1). Have students find other points (or an equation) that will result in a parabola containing the given points. They should justify and compare their answers, because many solutions are possible.

Adapted from "Cartoon Corner," *Mathematics Teaching in the Middle School*, November 2004, page 189, edited by Sue McMillen

3

Fractions, Decimals, and Percent

Closeness Counts in Horseshoes

Peanuts / by Charles Schulz

Peanuts, by Charles Schulz, 4/7/88. © United Feature Syndicate, Inc.

1. If Sally was getting closer, what might her first guess have been? Explain.

2. One way to get a close estimate for 2 1/2 × 2 1/2 is to round one number up to the next whole number, and the other number down to the previous whole number. What would be an estimate using that method? How does that result compare with the result from rounding both numbers up? Show your work below.

3. Draw a picture to show that 2 1/2 × 2 1/2 pizzas is 6 1/4 pizzas.

4. Draw a picture to show that 2 1/2 × 2 1/2 inches is 6 1/4 inches.

5. **Challenge:** Choose either pizza or inches, and show why 3 1/2 × 2 1/4 is 7 7/8.

Solutions

1. Any number larger than ten million would be further away.
2. The estimate would be 6; if you round one 2 1/2 up to 3 and the other 2 1/2 down to 2, you would multiply to find that 2 × 3 is 6. If you applied the traditional rule for rounding, you would round both numbers up to 3 and your estimate would be 3 × 3, or 9. This alternative way to round demonstrates that students should use number and operation sense rather than rules when rounding numbers for an estimate.

(*Teacher note:* Explanations and drawings may vary for the solutions to questions 3–5.)

3.

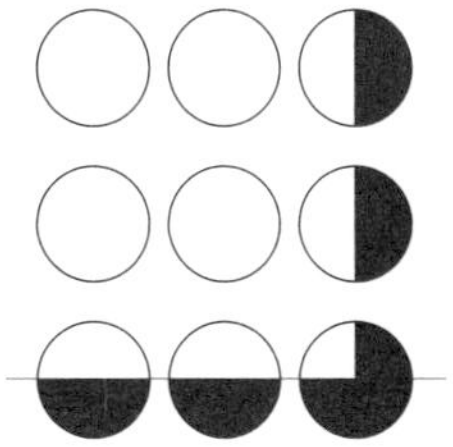

2 1/2 pizzas, 1 time

2 1/2 pizzas, 2 times

2 1/2 pizzas, 1/2 time

Counting whole and partial pieces gives 6 1/4 pizzas.

4.

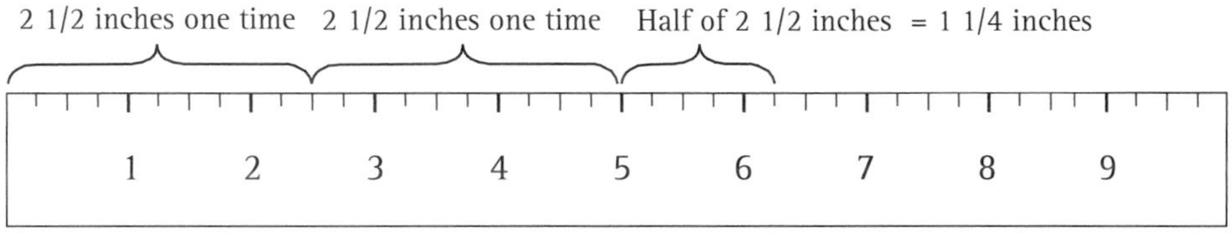

The final meaurement on the ruler shows 6 1/4 inches.

5. **Challenge:** Answers will vary, but drawings or explanations should be similar to the illustrations above.

Field-Test Comments

I teach 8th-grade math in a drop-out prevention school. Most of my students scored very low on our state test, and about 1/3 are in the Exceptional Student Education program. I used this cartoon after a lesson on multiplying fractions and mixed numbers. We had already drawn models to show multiplying fractions, so this activity fit right in.

Problems 1–4 were done by the whole group; students could do problem 5 alone or with their tablemates. A few students said they were confused by the activity, but the overall response was very positive. Most students said they enjoyed the activity and felt that other kids would enjoy it too.

Peggy Bodine
Clearwater Intermediate School
Clearwater, Florida

Other Ideas

- These problems can also be demonstrated easily with other real-world models, such as money, time, or egg cartons.

Adapted from "Cartoon Corner," *Mathematics Teaching in the Middle School,* February 2006, page 279, edited by Andy Reeves and Mary Lou Beasley

Have Some Pie!

For Better or For Worse **by Lynn Johnston**

1. Which piece is larger, 1/6 of the pie or 1/4 of the pie? How much larger?

2. The cartoon shows two large pieces, 1/3 and 1/4. After these two pieces are eaten, how much of the pie remains for the other four pieces?

3. Sara divides 1/2 of the blueberry pie into three pieces. One piece equals 1/3 of the whole pie, and the other two pieces are the same size as each other. How large is each of the smaller pieces? (Hint: draw a picture!)

4. **Challenge:** Would you rather have a serving that is 1/3 of an 8-inch pie or a serving that is 1/4 of a 9-inch pie? Show your work, and justify your answer.

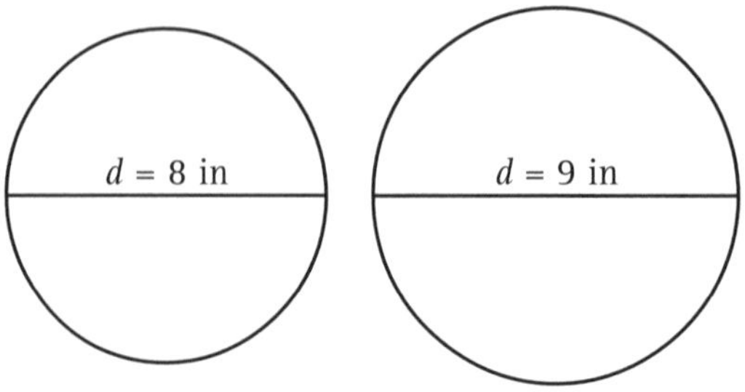

Solutions

1. One-fourth of the pie is larger; the difference between the two pieces is 1/12.
2. 5/12
3. Visually, if you continue to divide the pie into equal pieces that are the same size as the two smallest pieces shown, you will have 12 pieces and each piece will be 1/12 of the pie. See the drawing. Some students will solve the equation $1\ 2 + 1/3 + 2x = 1$ for x and also find that $x = 1/12$.

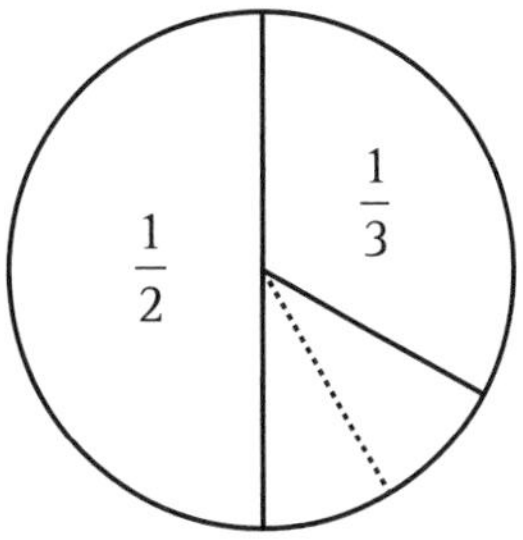

4. The area of an 8-inch pie (using 3.14 for pi) is about 50.2 square inches; the area of a 9-inch pie is about 63.9 square inches. Therefore, 1/3 of the 8-inch pie is about 16.7 square inches, and 1/4 of the 9-inch pie is about 16.0 square inches, which is a difference of less than 1 square inch. Since 1/3 of the 8-inch pie is a little bigger, some students may choose this piece.

Field-Test Comments

This cartoon was used with my average 8th-grade class in mid-November. The students related well to the assignment, as we had just reviewed fractions and Thanksgiving was approaching. One student gave a unique response to problem 4; she preferred the smaller piece with the comment "I'm on a diet!"

Jeanne Gagliardo
Safety Harbor Middle School
Safety Harbor, Florida

Other Ideas

- Break the class into groups, and have them use large paper and markers to illustrate their fraction calculations with pictures and computations. Then have each group share its results with the class. If you can make four groups, have each group illustrate one problem from questions 1–4. Otherwise, have each group do its own interpretation of all four problems.
- If you can use this activity around Thanksgiving, change the blueberry to "pumpkin" and illustrate the fractional parts with real pies. A pumpkin pie will cut "cleaner" than a blueberry one anyway. Be sure to have enough extra pies for everyone to have a taste when you are done.
- NCTM's Illuminations Web site has a number of resources to support conceptual learning of fractions. One example is http://illuminations.nctm.org/LessonDetail.aspx?id=L284.

Adapted from "Cartoon Corner," *Mathematics Teaching in the Middle School,* April 2002, page 444, edited by Kris Warloe

Loud, Louder, Loudest

1. If the sales tax is 5 percent, how much more would you pay in sales tax for the loudest mower than for the loud mower?

2. Sam buys one each of the three lawn mowers shown at a 25-percent-off sale for his lawn service business. If the sales tax is 7 percent, what is the total cost of the three mowers?

3. In a recent change in price–

   (a) the louder mower's price was reduced 20 percent. What is its new price?

   (b) the loud mower's price was increased 20 percent. What is its new price?

   (c) Which of these mowers is more expensive now? How much more?

4. Lawn mowers are a major contributor to noise pollution, which is measured in *decibels*. A typical gas-powered mower produces 90 decibels, whereas an electric-powered mower produces only about 55 decibels. What percent of decrease in decibels of noise pollution would this contributing factor be if everyone switched to an electric mower? Round your answer to the nearest whole percent.

Solutions

1. The difference is \$5.00: 0.05(149) = 7.45 and 0.05(249) = 12.45; and 12.45 - 7.45 = 5.00.
2. \$149.00 + \$195.00 + \$249.00 = \$593.00; \$593.00 × 75% = \$444.75, the sale price; \$444.75 × 1.07 = \$475.89, the price after tax is added.
3. The new price for the louder mower is (0.8)(195), or \$156.00. The new price of the loud mower is (1.20)(149), or \$178.80. The loud mower costs \$22.80 more than the louder one.
4. 39 percent; $\frac{90-55}{90} = \frac{35}{90} = 0.3888...$, or 39 percent.

Field-Test Comments

Two classes of Algebra I students were given this activity in mid-December as part of their bell work (the time at the beginning of class when I check attendance and homework). We had covered percent, sales tax, percent increase, and percent decrease several weeks earlier. The worksheet provided a nice review for these topics right before semester exams.

The cartoon sparked quite a conversation on lawn mowing, and even "Tim the Tool Man Taylor" was brought up and how he souped up lawn mowers. The only problem students had was reading the numbers in the cartoon—it might help to have these written on the board. The success rate ran around 80 percent on the four problems, indicating general success with the activity.

I really liked the questions for this cartoon and will use the cartoon again when we cover percent. To increase student success, I would refer them to the pages in the book and their specific notes. These questions could also be used as FCAT (Florida Comprehensive Assessment Test) review problems.

Pam Gretton
OakLeaf School
Orange Park, Florida

Other Ideas

- NCTM's Illuminations Web site has some basic conceptual activities for percent at http://illuminations.nctm.org/LessonDetail.aspx?id=L249.
- Collect newspaper ads from such stores as Sears, Home Depot, and Loew's, and have students cut out lawnmower ads to compare prices.
- Have students investigate the inventors of such household items as the lawn mower, electric doorbell, coat hanger, flyswatter, iron, and so on, and report to the class their findings.
- Have students investigate the decibel levels of other sounds, from voices to rock concerts, and the recommendations made by experts as to what levels are dangerous for humans.
- Some students might be interested in researching the United States Lawn Mower Racing Association, collecting such race data as speed and cost, and writing word problems for the other students to solve.

Adapted from "Cartoon Corner," *Mathematics Teaching in the Middle School*, March 2000, page 445, edited by Judith A. White

"Not So Hairy" Cut

Herman, by Jim Unger, 7-26-04. HERMAN® is reprinted with permission from LaughingStock Licensing Inc., Ottawa, Canada. All Rights Reserved.

1. A "dollar's worth" is what fractional part of a haircut?

2. If a "dollar's worth" haircut is trimming 237 hairs, how many hairs are on the gentleman's head? How do you know?

3. **Challenge:** The average number of hairs on a person's head depends on the hair color. Blonds have about 140,000 hairs; brunettes have about 108,000 hairs; and redheads have about 90,000 hairs. After a "dollar's worth" haircut, approximately how many uncut hairs would be left on a head of each color? Show your work below.

   Blonds: Brunettes: Redheads:

4. Human hair grows, on average, 1/2 inch a month. Each individual hair grows about 26 inches in its lifetime. At that rate, how long would an individual hair be alive and growing?

5. The *Guinness Book of World Records* reports the longest human hair length at 13 feet, 10 1/2 inches. At the normal growth rate, how long would a person take to grow hair that long?

HERMAN®

by Jim Unger

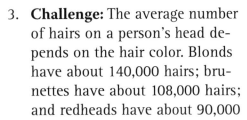

"Just cut off a dollar's worth."

Solutions

1. 1/3 haircut
2. 711 hairs
3. Blonds: 93,000 to 94,000. Brunettes: 72,000. Redheads: 60,000. Students would either find 1/3 of the hair-color number and subtract that result from the number, or find 2/3 of the hair-color number directly.
4. 52 months, or 4 years, 4 months. Mathematically, the problem is a real-world example of dividing by a fraction: 26 inches ÷ ½ inch/month = 52 months.
5. 333 months, or 27 years, 9 months. Converting 13 feet, 10 1/2 inches gives 166 1/2 inches. Calculating 166 1/2 inches ÷ 1/2 inch/month gives 333 months. Dividing by 12 months/year gives 27 years, 9 months.

Field-Test Comments

The cartoon and worksheet were used with academic-track math students in 8th grade in December as a review of previously learned material. It was an excellent format to assess basic proportional reasoning skills, which receives a lot of emphasis in middle-grades mathematics programs.

The students had no difficulty with questions 1 and 2, but some students were confused by question 3. Many of them used the information from question 2 (that a dollar's worth was trimming 237 hairs) and did not use a proportion to correctly determine how much a "dollar's worth" was for each hair color.

The last two questions posed no problems for my students. Question 5 was a good review for converting to similar units (feet, inches) before calculating a solution.

Kristen Dailey
Boardman Center Middle School
Boardman, Ohio

Other Ideas

- Students might enjoy taking a "Hair IQ Test" found at http://www.hairarchives.com/private/IQ.htm. Others might enjoy searching the Web for "hairy facts," such as the longest ear hairs ever recorded.

- Students might consider the problem of determining the number of hairs per square inch on their heads. They would take the number of hairs on their head—blond, brunette, or redhead, or some average of those numbers—and divide by the approximate number of square inches for the hair-growing part of their scalp. Approximating the latter would be an interesting challenge that might involve putting bowls on their heads, or making molds from aluminum foil, or using a formula.

Adapted from "Cartoon Corner," *Mathematics Teaching in the Middle School,* October 2005, page 132, prepared by Suzanne S. Austin-Hill, Hamp Sherard, and Diane F. White; edited by Andy Reeves and Mary Lou Beasley

Real-World Fractions

Tiger *by Bud Blake*

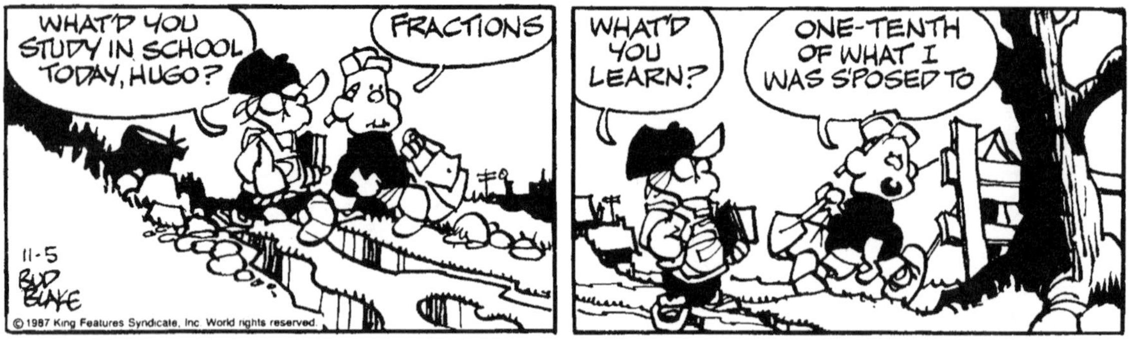

Tiger, by Bud Blake, 11/5/87. © King Features Syndicate. Used with permission. All Rights Reserved.

1. How would you rate Hugo's success with his fraction lesson? What part of the lesson did he *not* learn? Explain your thinking.

2. Write one-tenth as a fraction, a decimal, and a percent.

3. If Hugo had answered one-tenth of the questions on a forty-problem test correctly, how many problems would he have gotten correct? How many would he have missed? How do you know?

4. How would you explain to a third grader who is just starting to learn about fractions that 1/10 is smaller than 1/5 even though 10 is larger than 5? Can you use a real-world object to explain it?

5. **Challenge:** How do you spend your day? Estimate your activities for one typical Wednesday–sleeping, eating, attending school, studying, playing, watching television. Form fractions that express the amount of time you spend in each activity during the day. Convert the fractions to percents. On the back of this sheet, construct a circle graph to illustrate your results.

Solutions

1. 9/10 is what Hugo didn't learn.
2. 1/10, 0.1, and 10 percent
3. He would have gotten 4 correct and missed 36.
4. Answers will vary. Ideally students will solidify their knowledge by writing an explanation based on their own experiences. For example, they might say that if you cut a cake into ten pieces the same size, and an identical cake into five pieces the same size, each slice would be 1/10 and 1/5, respectively. And the 1/5 piece would be twice as big as the 1/10 piece. Encourage them to use a diagram to help with their explanation.
5. Answers will vary.

Field-Test Comments

I used this cartoon with my sixth graders in late November immediately after finishing a unit on decimals. We discussed that cartoons sometimes have hidden messages, and then we related Hugo's comment on learning 1/10 of what he should have to their recent test over decimals. The students then answered the questions on the worksheet individually but were encouraged to talk with one another as they worked.

Questions 1–3 were pretty easy for them. Several students remarked that Hugo actually had learned something about fractions because he knew that 1/10 was a small number. Question 4 generated a lot of discussion because it's difficult to fold paper into 5ths and 10ths and also find real-world objects divided "naturally" into those denominators. We could use metric rulers or base-ten blocks for 10ths and partition them ourselves into 5ths.

Students enjoyed question 5 the most, and particularly the explanations they made, because it forced them to think about what fractions actually meant. About half the students used decimals rather than fractions, however, because of our recent coverage, which seemed reasonable to me.

Tom Lewis
Hamilton School
Moline, Illinois

Other Ideas

- Have students write down some things about fractions that they think Hugo might not know. This exercise might allow them to express things they do not know themselves, but in a non-threatening way.
- Have students make a concept map about fractions, decimals, and percents, showing how these different ways to express numbers are linked.
- A lesson that ties together fractions, percents, and decimals can be found at http://illuminations.nctm.org/LessonDetail.aspx?id=L249.
- The Circle Grapher found at http://illuminations.nctm.org/ActivityDetail.aspx?ID=60 could be used for question 5, instead of students' making the graph on the back of their papers.

Adapted from "Cartoon Corner," *Mathematics Teaching in the Middle School,* January–March 1995, page 300, edited by Barbara Cain

Reciprocal Agreement

1. Why is Bark doing a handstand to explain *reciprocal* to Bite? Explain below.

2. What operation is associated with reciprocals?

3. What is the definition of the reciprocal of a number *x*?

Bark and Bite *by Judy White*

4. Give the reciprocal of each number below, if possible:

2/3: ____	4: ____	$2\frac{1}{2}$: ____	1: ____
−1/5: ____	3/8: ____	$3\frac{3}{4}$: ____	−3/5: ____
7/12: ____	−10: ____	0.5: ____	0: ____

5. What whole number does not have a reciprocal? _____
Explain why not below.

Solutions

1. Bark thinks that Bite will understand reciprocal better if he turns himself upside down, like you do with a fraction to produce its reciprocal. You interchange the numerator and denominator.
2. The operation is multiplication, but students might also say division since division of fractions is usually performed by multiplying by the reciprocal.
3. The reciprocal of x is the number you multiply x by to get 1.
4. The answers are in **bold** below.

2/3: **3/2**	4: **1/4**	$2\frac{1}{2}$: **2/5**	1: **1**
–1/5: **–5 or -5/1**	3/8: **8/3**	$3\frac{3}{4}$: **4/15**	–3/5: **–5/3**
7/12: **12/7**	–10: **–1/10**	0.5: **2**	0: **N/A**

5. Zero has no reciprocal. There is no number that, when multiplied by 0, gives 1.

Field-Test Comments

This activity was given to my 7th-grade Algebra I Honors (gifted) students in mid-November. They had recently finished solving equations with fractional coefficients, so the activity was a reminder of the work they had previously done. The cartoon could have been used as an alternative form of assessment. An extension idea would be to add a problem on finding the reciprocal of several algebraic fractions.

Bennie Royal Smith
Baypoint Middle School
St. Petersburg, Florida

Other Ideas

- If you feel that students will be thrown off by negative numbers or mixed numbers, then cover the negative signs or replace the mixed numbers with other fractions.
- You might have advanced students investigate dividing fractions without using the reciprocal. For example, you can divide fractions using

$$a/b \div c/d = (a \div c)/(b \div d),$$

making the division algorithm similar to the multiplication algorithm. You usually have to rename the first fraction so that $a \div c$ or $b \div d$, or both, is a whole number. If you have to rename both $a \div c$ and $b \div d$, then you wind up with the same process as if you invert and multiply. So the process is not necessarily faster; however, it can lead to the interesting realization that the algorithm we all use is certainly not the only one that works.

Adapted from "Cartoon Corner," *Mathematics Teaching in the Middle School,* May 2000, page 594, edited by Judith A. White

Salary by the Point

Ziggy *by Tom Wilson*

1. Suppose that Ziggy names a salary of $1234 per hour. After the boss positions the decimal point, rounding to the nearest cent, what are his possible hourly salaries? Circle the most reasonable one in your list.

2. If Ziggy is scheduled to work 40 hours each week, what will his weekly salary be using the most reasonable salary rate from problem 1?

3. There are 52 weeks in a year. Ziggy gets 2 weeks of unpaid vacation each year. How much will he make in a year?

4. If Ziggy saves 5 percent of what he earns, how much will he save in a year?

5. During 1 week, Ziggy works 45 hours. His regular wage is the one from problem 2. If he earns time and a half for each hour that he works over 40 hours, how much will he earn that week? ("Time and a half" means he gets paid 1½ times his normal hourly rate.)

6. **Challenge:** Together, three friends earn $32.10 per hour. If Mark earns $2.35 more per hour than Joaquin, and Sasha earns $0.65 per hour less than Mark, how much does each friend earn?

Solutions

1. The possible hourly rates are \$1234.00, \$123.40, \$12.34, \$1.23, and \$0.12 per hour; \$12.34 should be circled.
2. His weekly salary will be \$493.60. Multiply \$12.34/hour × 40 hours/week.
3. He will make \$24,680. Multiply \$493.60/week × 50 weeks.
4. He will save \$1234.00. Multiply \$24.680 × 0.05. Some students will notice that this is the original number he gave his boss. You might explore why this is true, or humorously ask why they went through all that work just to get the number Ziggy started with.
5. He will earn \$586.15. For the first 40 hours, he makes his weekly salary of \$493.60. For the other 5 hours, he makes $1\frac{1}{2}$ × \$12.34/hr., or 1.5 × \$12.34/hr., giving \$92.55. The total is \$586.15.
6. Mark earns \$11.70, Joaquin earns \$9.35, and Sasha earns \$11.05. Students can set up an equation letting M, $M - 2.35$, and $M - 0.65$ be the hourly rates of Mark, Joaquin, and Sasha respectively. Solving $M + (M - 2.35) + (M - 0.65) = 32.10$ gives $M = \$11.70$. Joaquin's and Sasha's rates are determined from Mark's. Some students will solve the problem by using the *guess-check-revise* approach.

Field-Test Comments

We used this activity with 6th-grade regular and 7th-grade advanced math classes in late September. The 6th graders got the humor in the cartoon, understood what would be a reasonable salary, and had varying degrees of success from there on depending on their familiarity with percent, number of weeks in a year, time and a half, and so forth.

The 7th graders got the first five rather easily. Even though we had been working with translating word problems into equations, many solved the challenge problem using *guess-check-revise.* A few students wrote an equation with three variables and then substituted to get an equation with only one variable. It was a great way to get the students thinking about equations solved this way, and students were assigned two similar homework problems as a follow-up.

We recommend using the cartoon as a class activity where the students can work in collaborative groups so students can exchange ideas.

Rhody Gecan and Yvette DeRollo
Southside Fundamental Middle School
St. Petersburg, Florida

Other Ideas

- Students might profit from finding the minimum wage at the present time and setting up a problem in which they compare what they would make over a lifetime working a minimum-wage job versus Ziggy's rate.
- Problem 2 could be extended to take Ziggy's weekly earnings and deduct typical amounts for taxes, Social Security, health insurance, and so forth, to determine what he has left to spend.
- Problem 2 could be modified by taking his savings each week and investing it with an assumed rate of return. How much would his savings grow into in 5 years? In 10 years? In 40 years? A spreadsheet would be an appropriate way to analyze such a situation.

Adapted from "Cartoon Corner," *Mathematics Teaching in the Middle School,* May 2003, page 483, edited by Sue McMillen

"Supperman"

1. Why do the diners need to find 15 percent of their bill? Explain.

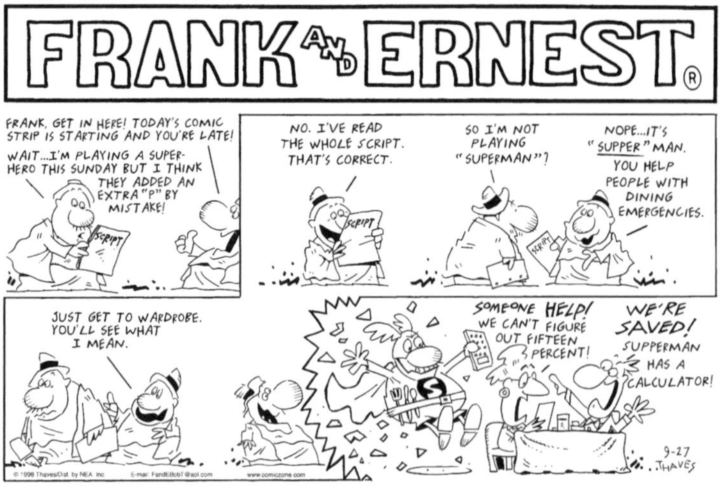

Frank and Ernest, by Bob Thaves, 9/27/98. © Thaves/Dist. By Newspaper Enterprise Association, Inc.

2. If Supperman had not arrived with his calculator, what other methods could the diners have used to compute 15 percent of their bill? Give at least two methods for a bill of $45, one of which uses only mental mathematics. (Use the back of the page if needed.)

3. Supperman calculated the 15 percent tip to be exactly $6.36. What was the amount of the bill that the waiter presented?

4. If Supperman had suggested that the diners leave $90 for the combined bill and 15 percent tip, how much would the meal have cost?

5. If you receive excellent service, you usually leave a 20 percent tip. Explain how to compute 20 percent of a bill mentally.

Solutions

1. They need to compute the tip.
2. Answers will vary. Some possibilities are these:
   - Use mental math to calculate 10 percent of $45 as $4.50, then halve that amount, getting $2.25, for 5 percent. Add the two amounts to get $6.75.
   - Change 15 percent to a decimal, and multiply $45 by 0.15.
   - Change 15 percent to the fraction 15/100, and multiply by $45.
   - Use the proportion $15/100 = n/45$, and solve for n.
3. The bill amount was $42.40. Some students will solve $0.15x = \$6.36$ for x, the cost of the meal. Some might take 1/3 of $6.36 as $2.12, then double that amount to $4.24, which is 10 percent of the meal. Moving the decimal point one place to the right gives the cost of the meal as $42.40. Other methods will also emerge.
4. The meal cost was $78.26. A one-step solution is to realize that the meal multiplied by 115%, or 1.15, gives the cost of the meal and tip. So solving $1.15x = \$90$ gives $78.26.
5. Answers will vary. Some possibilities are these:
   - Find 10 percent by moving the decimal point, then doubling that amount.
   - Find 10 percent by finding 1/10 mentally, then doubling that amount.
   - Find 20 percent by computing 0.20 times the cost of the meal.

Field-Test Comments

I presented the cartoon to 8th graders in the context of a review of our work with percent in 7th grade. This problem also goes well with a strand of our algebra book dealing with proportions that we work on each week, so it felt like it would be good practice. Students understood the humor, although they did mention "Supperman" not being so super if he needed to use a calculator.

Students recalled the three types of percent problems, two of which are covered here—finding a percent of a given amount (question 1) and finding an amount that 15 percent is of a given amount (question 2). Question 3, the hardest one on the worksheet, caused lots of discussion. Few students actually got to question 4 in the 40 minutes we had. One pair of students understood the idea of 115 percent including the bill and the tip, and they explained it to the class. No one got to question 5, which seems easier than the others.

Interesting note: Because of our location—San Francisco—students thought 15 percent was a low tip and that 20 percent was the standard tip. Many students knew that doubling our sales tax gives you about 17 percent, which appears to be a way many of their parents figure out their tip. Many others already knew the 10-percent-and-half-of-10-percent method for finding 15 percent. Overall, a very good practice and discussion about real-world math.

Glenn Kenyon
San Francisco School
San Francisco, California

Other Ideas

Students might enjoy surveying adults to find out their tipping habits for meals, and analyze the results. They could first generate a list of common questions to ask, such as, "Have you ever worked as a waiter, and how would this experience affect your tipping habits?"

Adapted from "Cartoon Corner," *Mathematics Teaching in the Middle School,* February 2000, page 388, edited by Judith A. White

To Sleep or Not to Sleep, That Is the Question

Shoe *by Chris Cassatt and Gary Brookins*

1. How many minutes is Shoe awake during 3 percent of a day?

2. How many seconds are in 3 percent of a week?

3. How many hours and minutes are you awake on an average day? What percent of a 24-hour day is that?

4. Draw a line graph below to represent the age of a child from birth to age 15, and what percent of an average day is spent sleeping. Explain what happens to change the percent over time.

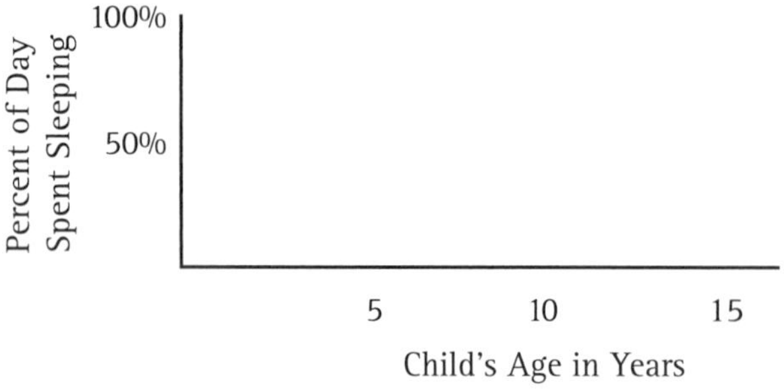

Explanation:

5. Draw a new line graph that compares the child's age with the percent of an average day that he/she is awake. How is this graph different from the one above?

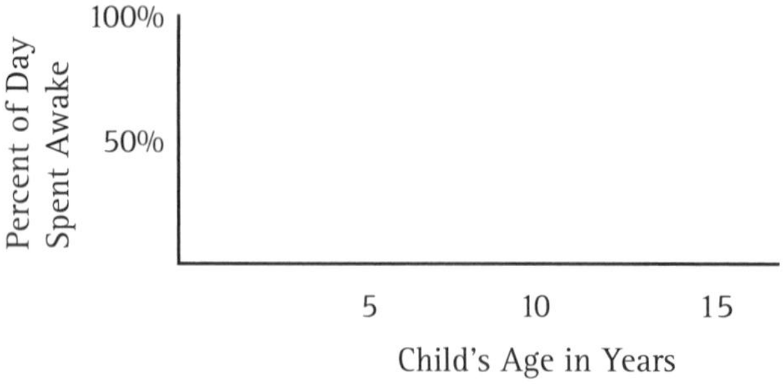

Explanation:

Solutions

1. Three percent of 24 hours, or 1,440 minutes, is 43.2 minutes or 43 minutes, 12 seconds.
2. Calculate (0.03)(7 days/week)(24 hours/day)(60 minutes/hour)(60 seconds/minute), giving 18,144 seconds/week.
3. Answers will vary. If a student sleeps 8 hours/day, the percent of time awake would be 66-2/3 percent.
4. Answers will vary. The graph should show a high percent of sleep time for a newborn—perhaps 75 percent—then come down until the child reaches school age. It would come down more slowly from then until he or she reached age 15. This graph would show a negative correlation, since sleep time decreases as age increases.
5. Answers will vary. The graph would show a low percent of time awake as an infant, then gradually increase as age increases. This graph would be inversely related to the one in question 4, having a positive correlation between age and time awake.

Field-Test Comments

My Algebra I class had covered percent a few weeks earlier, so we used this activity as a review and warm-up. We read the cartoon together accompanied by lots of groans. Expect (and enjoy) the conversations that will emerge about the lack of sleep many of these students get.

Around 80 percent of the students were successful with problems 1–3. They weren't as successful with the graphs in problems 4 and 5—they understood the concept but had difficulty showing it with line graphs—they wanted to draw bar graphs instead. This was disappointing from a teacher standpoint, but several students did mention that question 5 was just the opposite of question 4.

This activity was a nice application of what we had learned. It taught me a lot about how much direction even advanced students really need. I suggest reminding students in advance of the parts of a graph, and referring them to the text as a resource.

Pam Gretton
OakLeaf School
Orange Park, Florida

Other Ideas

1. Students might enjoy doing problems 4 and 5 of this activity at home with their parents' input about their own sleep time.
2. Students could extend the graphs in problems 4 and 5 by asking older adults what their sleep patterns were beyond age 15. Probably students will find that as adults reach retirement years, their percent of sleep time increases.

Adapted from "Cartoon Corner," *Mathematics Teaching in the Middle School,* November 2005, page 182, edited by Mary Lou Beasley and Andy Reeves

Untimely Sales

ZIGGY *by Tom Wilson*

1. How do you think Ziggy interpreted the sign? Explain.

2. If a watch is 25 percent off as the salesman describes, and it is set at 12:00 noon, what possible times will the watch show twenty-four hours later?

3. If a watch is 20 percent off as the salesman describes, and it is set at 12:00 noon, what possible times will the watch show twenty-four hours later? If it is 30 percent off?

4. If you bought a watch at this store and it lost 4 hours between 12:00 noon and 12:00 midnight, would it fit into the range of 25–30 percent off? Explain your thinking.

Solutions

1. Ziggy thought that the percent off referred to the price of the watch, not its precision.
2. The watch will read 6:00. It will be either 25 percent fast or 25 percent slow, and 25 percent of 24 hours is 6 hours. So the watch will show either 6 hours before 12:00 noon or 6 hours after 12:00 noon. In either instance, it will read 6:00.
3. The reasoning is similar to that in question 2. At 20 percent of 24 hours, the watch gains or loses 4.8 hours, which is 4 hours, 48 minutes. So the watch would read either 7:12 (a.m.) or 4:48 (p.m.). At 30 percent, the watch would gain or lose 7.2 hours, or 7 hours, 12 minutes. So it would read either 4:48 (a.m.) or 7:20 (p.m.).
4. A watch that loses 4 hours in a 12-hour span is losing time at a rate of 33 1/3 percent, so it would not fit into the 25–30 percent range.

Field-Test Comments

This activity was used for a nonroutine problem-solving day in mid-November in an Algebra I class. These students are good with percents related to money because they see percent used that way most often. They struggled somewhat with percent related to *time* due to its unfamiliarity, but this was a good method of having them consider percents used in another fashion. Even advanced students are sometimes resistant to writing in math class, and some struggled explaining their thoughts. However, they need to learn to do that, so the worksheet was useful in that regard.

Bennie Royal Smith
Baypoint Middle School
St. Petersburg, Florida

Other Ideas

- Students might set up an experiment to see how slow or fast their own watch is, and convert that time into a percent. That would mean choosing a timepiece as the "standard," which is assumed to be correct. They might choose the classroom clock, for example. Or they could search the Internet to find Greenwich Mean Time, and use that time because it is accepted around the world.
- Another enjoyable excursion is to search the Web for the scientific definition of a second as a unit of time.

Adapted from "Cartoon Corner," *Mathematics Teaching in the Middle School,* November–December 1995, page 552, edited by Barbara Cain

4

Geometry and Measurement

Around the World in 80 Days?

"Around the world in 80 days?
Boy that guy was SLOW!"

The Family Circus, by Bil Keane, 7/15/04. © Bil Keane, Inc., King Features Syndicate. Used with permission. All Rights Reserved.

1. The circumference of the Earth at the equator is 24,901.55 miles. If a person traveled the Earth's circumference in 80 days, what was the average distance traveled per day?

2. A supersonic transport plane (SST) travels at about 1,350 mph. How long would it take an SST to travel the circumference of the Earth?

3. What is the diameter of the Earth?

4. Saturn's diameter at its equator is about 74,900 miles. Covered wagons took about 166 days to travel 3000 miles. If it were possible to travel around the equator of Saturn in a covered wagon, how long would the trip take? Give your answer to the nearest month.

5. The Space Shuttle can travel 3000 miles in 8 minutes. At that speed it would take the Space Shuttle about 3 hours and 57 minutes to travel the circumference of Jupiter. What is the approximate circumference of Jupiter? Round to the nearest thousand.

Solutions

1. The average distance traveled is about 311 miles per day.
2. An SST would take about 18.4 hours (8 hours and 27 minutes) to make the trip.
3. The diameter of the Earth is about 7926 miles: 24901.55 = 2 ≈ r; $r \approx 3963$; $d \approx 7926$.
4. The trip would take about 11 years and 4 months.

   $\frac{74900}{3000} = \frac{x}{166}$ $x \approx 4144$ days
5. The circumference of Jupiter is about 88,900 miles.

   $\frac{237}{8} = \frac{x}{3000}$

   $x = 88{,}875$ miles

Field-Test Comments

I used this activity with my eighth-grade prealgebra class to reinforce and extend recent lessons on measurement conversion, circles, and setting up proportions. I opened the lesson with the cartoon on the overhead projector, and the students immediately had lots of ideas and positive memories of reading the book or seeing the movie. After some background discussion, I sent them to work in groups with the worksheet.

When the predetermined time for group work had passed, each group selected a question to present to the class. I was delighted to see their successful application of recently taught concepts. Students enjoyed some impromptu sharing about the impact of rounding on their final answers and the degree of accuracy that makes sense in different situations. This activity provided me with a nice informal assessment of student understandings, and the students particularly enjoyed the science connections.

Anita Finn
Learning Prep School
West Newton, Massachusetts

Other Ideas

- Students might enjoy problems like the following:
  - If a 5-foot-tall student walked around the Earth at the equator, how much farther would her head move than her feet?
  - Suppose a rope is wrapped around the Earth at the equator. The rope is cut, and 3 more feet of rope is added. Suppose the new rope is exactly the same distance away from the equator at all points, so it still circles the Earth. Which of the following would fit under the rope? You? Your cat? Your pet snake?
- For other activities related to space travel, visit NCTM's Illuminations Web site at http://illuminations.nctm.org/LessonDetail.aspx?id=L254, http://illuminations.nctm.org/LessonDetail.aspx?id=L281, and http://illuminations.nctm.org/ActivityDetail.aspx?ID=119.

Adapted from "Cartoon Corner," *Mathematics Teaching in the Middle School,* April 2005, page 404, edited by Sue McMillen

Don't Sleep the Mileage

BEETLE BAILEY ® **By Mort Walker**

1. How many gallons of gasoline are needed to drive 200 miles in the jeep? In the tank? Show your work.

2. What does MPG mean? What factors might affect a vehicle's MPG ratio?

3. Search the Web for information on your favorite car or truck. What is the MPG for this vehicle? If more than one number is given, tell what the numbers mean and why one might be higher than the other.

4. How many gallons of gasoline are needed to drive your favorite vehicle to and from a family reunion 200 miles away? Use the current price of a gallon of gasoline to calculate the fuel cost for this trip.

Solutions

1. Approximately 15.4 gallons for the jeep; approximately 333.3 gallons for the tank
2. MPG means "miles per gallon." Factors that affect MPG are the weight and shape of the vehicle and the size and type of engine. (A hybrid vehicle is powered by both gasoline and electricity and so should use less gasoline.) Other factors are the amount of air in the tires, the accessories being run (such as air conditioning), the type of driving–city or highway, and the way the driver handles the car.
3. Usually both the highway and city MPG are listed, as determined by government tests under ideal conditions. Individual drivers can rarely expect to get numbers this high.
4. Answers will vary according to the type of vehicle. It might be interesting to have your students share their results for different types of cars and trucks.

Field-Test Comments

I used the cartoon as an opener for the day's lesson with seventh graders in December. My students were in the middle of a unit about finding unit rates when I presented them with the cartoon, so it fit right in with what we were doing. The cartoon gave them a context for what we were studying, and since we are in a military town, it connected our studies with families' lives in a personal way as well. Some of the students even began to comment and wonder about the amount of fuel other types of vehicles used as they traveled.

The cartoon might make a good springboard into researching fuel usage for other vehicles, and even a look into alternative fuels and their energy yields. Middle school students are interested in the environment, and this might catch their interest.

Gail Englert
Ruffner Academy, Norfolk Public Schools
Norfolk, Virginia

Other Ideas

- Students might ask their parents for the mileage estimate for their own family vehicle, and the average number of miles driven each year. Then they could calculate how much the family will spend for gasoline per year, and over the life of the car. All these situations involve estimating in a real-world sense.
- Interested students might research how people in other countries deal with the fact that gasoline costs are much higher in most countries than in the United States. Do people drive smaller cars, or use more bicycles and scooters, or use mass transportation?

Adapted from "Cartoon Corner," *Mathematics Teaching in the Middle School,* January 1999, page 245, edited by Julie A. Fisher

Keeping Track

1. What is the diameter of the table in feet if 478 laps equal a mile? (Use 3.14 for π, and round your answer to tenths.)

2. Suppose that three lanes, each 3 feet wide, surround the table. Runners run down the center of each lane. After ten laps, how much farther would the runner in the outside lane travel than the runner in the inside lane?

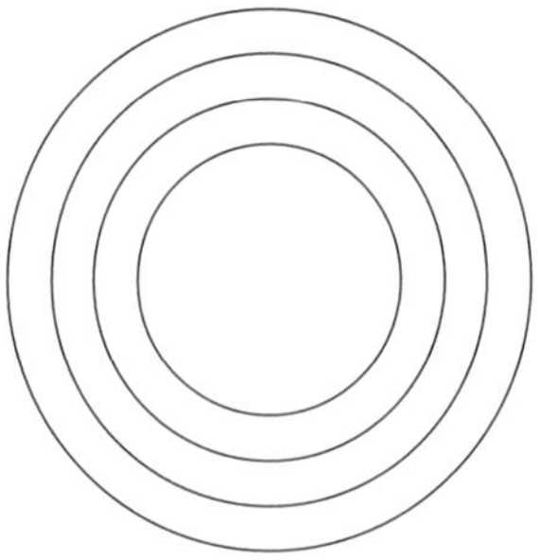

Close to Home *by John McPherson*

"I figured out that 478 times around the table is a mile."

3. **Challenge:** If the table above is 3 feet tall, how many square feet of fabric are needed to make the tablecloth? (Use 3.14 for π, and round to tenths.)

Solutions

1. 3.5 feet. Calculate 5280 feet/mile ÷ 478 laps = 11.05 feet/lap as circumference C of the table. Because $C = \pi d$, $d = 11.05/\pi$, or approximately 3.5 feet.
2. In the inner lane, the person would travel $\pi d = \pi(3.5 + 3)$, or 20.41 feet per lap, or 204.1 feet for 10 laps. In the outer lane, the person would travel $\pi d = \pi(3.5 + 3 + 3 + 3 + 3 + 3)$, or 58.09 feet per lap, or 580.9 feet for 10 laps. The difference is 580.9 – 204.1 = 376.8 feet.
3. The tablecloth is made up of the circle on top and the rectangle that goes around it.
4. Total Surface Area = area of circle + area of rectangle = $\pi r + 3 \bullet C$, where r is the radius of the circle and C is the circumference of the circle (or π times the diameter):
5. $$\begin{aligned} SA &= 3.14 \bullet (1.75)^2 + 3 \bullet 3.14 \bullet 3.5 \\ &= 9.61625 + 32.97 \\ &= 42.58625, \end{aligned}$$
   or about 42.6 square feet.

Field-Test Comments

This activity was used for a nonroutine problem-solving day in mid-November, in an Algebra I class. The students stumbled over some of the wording of the problems, but class discussion cleared up most of their difficulty. When students are covering diameter, circumference, and surface area, the activity might be quite useful as an enrichment worksheet in a collaborative group setting.

Bennie Royal Smith
Baypoint Middle School
St. Petersburg, Florida

Other Ideas

- Have students measure some tables in your classroom, and determine how many laps around them would make a 100-meter dash or a 1000-meter race.
- The standard lane width for most high school and college outdoor tracks in the United States is 42 inches. Have students calculate the offset distances for runners in each lane in a race of a particular length. (See the Web site http://www.sciencenews.org/articles/20030809/mathtrek.asp for help.)

Adapted from "Cartoon Corner," *Mathematics Teaching in the Middle School,* March–April 1998, page 434, edited by Julie Fisher

The Meal Mat

1. What is the mathematical term for the distance around a circle?

2. Heathcliff is sitting on a circular rug. If the diameter of the rug is 10 feet, what is the circumference of the rug?

3. The rug has a border that is 3 inches wide. The border is inside the 10-foot diameter. What is the area of the border?

HEATHCLIFF

"IF YOU STEP INSIDE THE PERIMETER, HE THINKS YOU'RE GOING TO FEED HIM."

Heathcliff, 2/10/05. By permission of George Gately and Creators Syndicate, Inc.

4. **Challenge:** The rug is in a rectangular room that is 12 feet wide and 15 feet long. The room has been emptied of furniture. If Heathcliff sits at a randomly selected spot on the floor, what is the probability that he is sitting on the rug? Make a top-view sketch of the rug and the room.

Solutions

(Teacher note: Answers were found using the pi key. If 3.14 is used, the answers will be slightly different.)

1. The distance around a circle is called the *circumference*.
2. The circumference is 31.42 feet. $C = 2\pi r = 2\pi(5) \approx 31.42$ feet.
3. The area of entire rug is 78.54 square feet ($5^2\pi$).
4. Since 3 inches is 0.25 feet, the radius of the circular section without the border is 4.75 feet. So the area of the part without the border is 70.88 square feet ($4.75^2\pi$). The area of the border is 7.66 square feet (78.54 – 70.88 = 7.66).
5. The area of the room is 180 square feet. The area of the rug is 78.54 square feet. So the probability of being on the rug is 78.54/180 = 0.436, or 43.6 percent.

Field-Test Comments

This activity was field-tested in Caitlin Ianonne's seventh-grade class of mixed ability levels, in mid-November. The students were familiar with the term *circumference* but had not used it in a long time and didn't understand it well. Basically they could do problems 1 and 2 successfully, but since they were interested in the cartoon, the teacher was able to re-introduce them to area and probability, the math concepts at the heart of problems 3 and 4, more effectively.

We would suggest that teachers have a prior discussion with the class and put familiar formulas on the board. We would also suggest that they draw "top down" views for problems 2–4.

Caitlin Ianonne
Grabiarz Middle School
Buffalo, New York
and
Sue McMillen
Buffalo State College
Buffalo, New York

Other Ideas

- Challenge students to find the dimensions of a room in which Heathcliff would have only a 28 percent chance of being on the rug.
- Challenge students to find the dimensions of the rectangular room that give Heathcliff the largest possible chance of being on the rug, and explain.
- Ask students to find the area of a circular rug that has a circumference of 20 feet.
- Ask students to find the circumference of a rug that has an area of 42 square feet.
- For activities that develop the concept of pi as a constant, visit NCTM's Illuminations Web site at http://illuminations.nctm.org/LessonDetail.aspx?id=U159 and http://illuminations.nctm.org/LessonDetail.aspx?id=L697.

Adapted from "Cartoon Corner," *Mathematics Teaching in the Middle School,* January 2004, page 268, edited by Sue McMillen

Running Patterns

1. Use the back of this paper and a scale of 1 centimeter equals 1 yard. Place a dot in the lower-left corner of the paper to represent Jason's starting position. Put a second dot at Jason's position at 10 yards out and a third dot at his final position of 10 yards to the right. Measure the distance between Jason's starting position and final position, and use your scale to express your answer to the nearest tenth of a yard.

2. Use a calculator to express $10\sqrt{2}$ to the nearest tenth.

3. Use a protractor and your scale drawing to measure 45 degrees from the same starting point. Measure $10\sqrt{2}$ centimeters along the diagonal. Is Jason in the same final position?

4. Assume Jason moves only forward (vertically) or to the right (horizontally). Find three other routes that Jason might take to get to the same final position of 10 yards out and 10 yards to the right. Give angle measures and distances, and have other students check your examples.

ROUTE 1 ROUTE 2 ROUTE 3

a) What is the longest possible route?
b) The shortest possible route?

Solutions

For questions 1 and 3, see the following diagram.

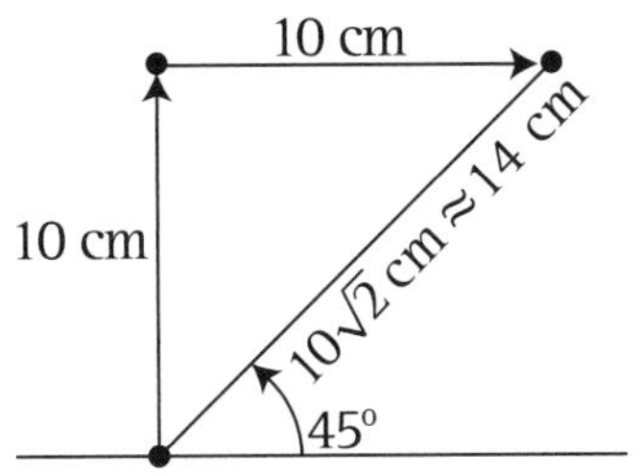

1. About 14.1 yards
2. With a calculator, $\sqrt{2} = 1.41$, so $10\sqrt{2} \approx 14.1$.
3. The position will be the same; therefore, Jason can run 20 yards following the directions, or 14.1 yards by taking the "shortest cut."
4. (a) The longest possible route is 20 yards. His runs vertically must total 10 yards and his runs horizontally must total 10 yards, but he could take a number of routes in making those distances.
   (b) The shortest possible route is the hypotenuse of the "10 up and 10 out" triangle, approximately 14.1 yards.

Field-Test Comments

I used this activity in December with eighth-grade algebra students during a 45-minute class period. Students were familiar with irrational numbers and had studied measurement and angles in previous years, though it has not been part of our class work this year. So it was a review of measurement and using protractors in a problem with some higher-thinking aspects.

Initially I gave each student a small piece of graph paper and asked them to create a 10 × 10 square. Then students were asked to draw several routes from the bottom-left corner of the large square to the upper-right corner, moving only up or to the right and drawing only on the graph-paper lines. After students had drawn several routes, we compared them and saw that any route under those conditions would travel a distance of 20 units. During discussion, students were able to determine that this distance could be reduced only if the rules were changed to allow routes that did not follow the lines of the graph paper. This exploration helped prepare students for the activity by asking them to think about different paths and what would make a path shorter or longer.

Dave Johnston
Luna Middle School
San Antonio, Texas

Other Ideas

- Assume Jason can move only forward horizontally or vertically in two-yard increments. How many different paths can he take to get to his final position at 10 yards out and 10 yards to the right? Use graph paper, and try easier examples of 2 yards out and 2 yards to the right; 4 yards out and 4 yards to the right. Look for a pattern.
- Students might enjoy using Logo to program a turtle to run hypothetical routes. This activity could be done using http://illuminations.nctm.org/ActivityDetail.aspx?ID=83.

Adapted from "Cartoon Corner," *Mathematics Teaching in the Middle School,* November 2000, page 175, edited by Judith A. White

Time and Time Again

The Middletons *by Ralph Dunagin and Dana Summers*

The Middletons, by Ralph Dunagin and Dana Summers, 2/12/94. © Tribune Media Services, Inc. All Rights Reserved. Reprinted with permission.

1. Wilson is confused about telling time. What is the correct answer to the question?

2. An error was made regarding the hands of the clock. Can you identify this error?

3. At what exact time is the hour hand actually on the 12? Write your answer the way this time would appear on a digital clock.

4. What do the following times, both a.m. and p.m., have in common?

   1:05; 2:11; 3:16; 4:22; 5:27; 6:33; 7:38; 8:44; 9:49; 10:55; 12:00

   For each time above, draw the hour and minute hands on a clock below. Then give your answer.

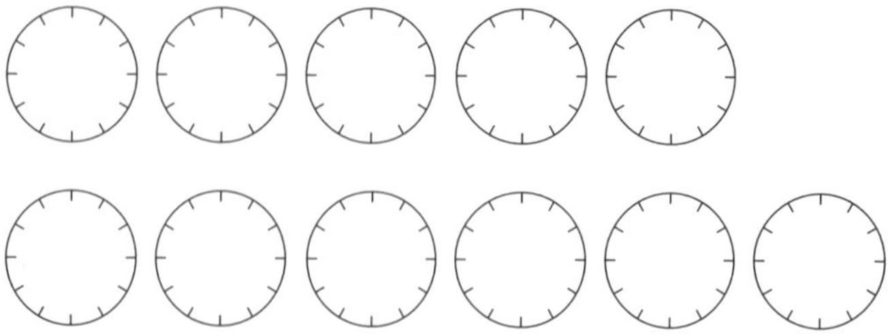

5. **Challenge:** How many times will the hands on a clock overlap during a day? A month? A year?

Solutions

1. 11:55, or 5 minutes until 12:00
2. The error is that the little hand should not actually be "on" the 12 at 11:55. It should be close to, but slightly to the left of, 12.
3. 12:00
4. The times, rounded to the nearest minute, show when the hour and minute hands overlap. Students should discover this occurrence after drawing hands on the first few clocks.
5. The hands will overlap 2 × 11, or 22, times each day; 7 × 22, or 154, times a week; and 365 × 22, or 8,030, times per year.

Field-Test Comments

I used this cartoon with my sixth-grade class in late November. We started with a brief discussion of the differences between digital and analog clocks. Then we read the cartoon. I asked the students what mistake Wilson had made. The kids could quickly tell what the proper time was for question 1. For question 2 they decided that Wilson had made a natural error by using an incorrect pattern (10 meant 10 minutes, so 11 means 11 minutes). They also knew that Wilson didn't really understand what the numbers actually stood for on the clock.

For question 4, I started by asking them if they saw any sort of pattern. We looked at the times in two ways, first as digital time. Did they see any patterns in the digits? They could see that several of the times had minutes that were doubles (e.g., :44, :33, etc.), but there wasn't anything that was common to them all. Next we looked at the times as they would appear on an analog clock. I reminded them of the way they had answered the question about when the hour hand pointed directly at the 12. I asked them to look at the time that would be the easiest to picture (12:00) and think about what was special about that time. They came up with several suggestions, and then were to apply their suggestions to the other times. Several students were eventually able to correctly state the answer about the hands overlapping.

Tom Lewis
Hamilton School
Moline, Illinois

Other Ideas

- Use one straight line to divide a clockface into two sections with the sum of the numbers the same in both sections. Then use two lines to divide the clockface into three sections, each with the same sum. Answers are shown below.

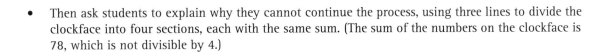

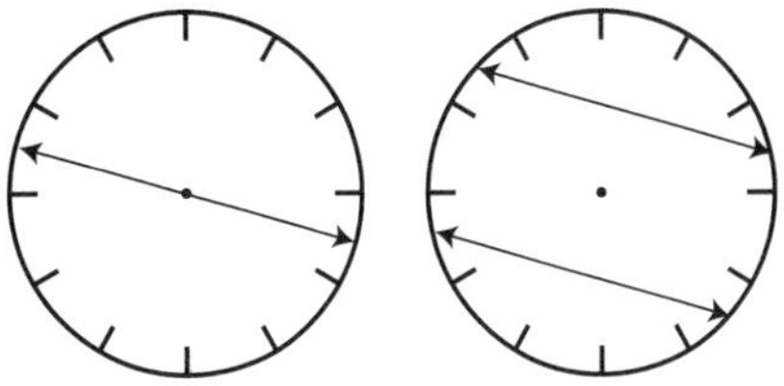

- Then ask students to explain why they cannot continue the process, using three lines to divide the clockface into four sections, each with the same sum. (The sum of the numbers on the clockface is 78, which is not divisible by 4.)

Adapted from "Cartoon Corner," *Mathematics Teaching in the Middle School,* November–December 1994, page 226, edited by Barbara Cain

A Square by Any Other Name

Luann

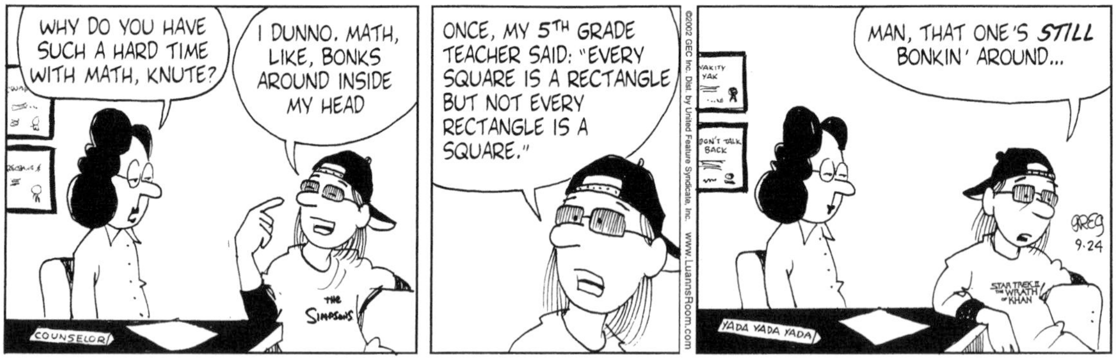

Luann, by Greg Evans. © GEC Inc./Dist. By United Feature Syndicate, Inc.

1. Look at the shape Gabriel made on his geoboard. Explain how you know his shape is a square.

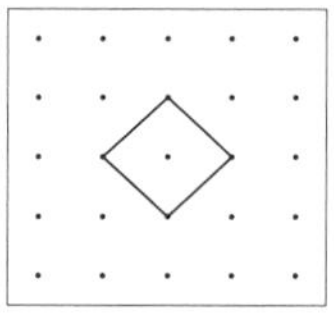

2. Use a geoboard to make a shape that meets each description, if possible. If it is not possible, explain why not.

   a. A rectangle that is not a square

   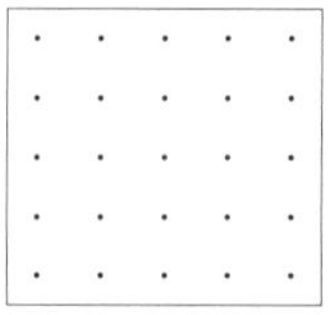

   b. A square that is not a rectangle

   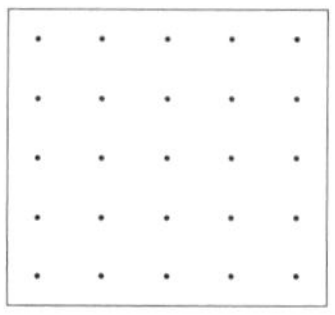

   c. A rectangle that is not a parallelogram

   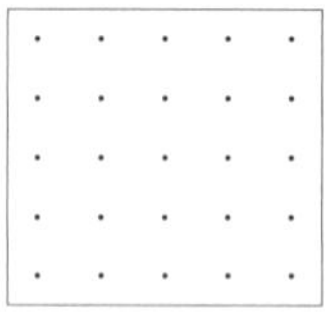

   d. A parallelogram that is not a rectangle

   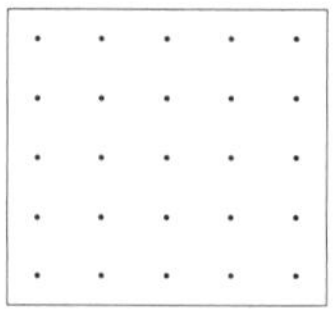

   e. A quadrilateral that is not a trapezoid

   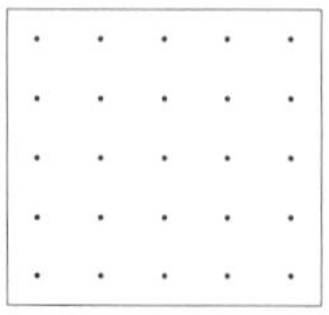

   f. An isosceles triangle that is not equilateral

   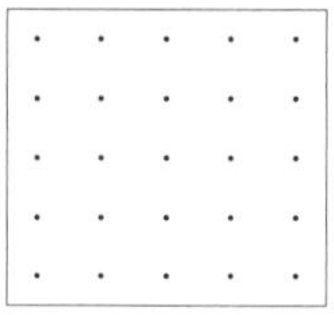

Solutions

1. The sides are all the same length: 1 diagonal unit. If you measure the angles, they are 90 degrees.
2. Answers will vary, but students should conclude that shapes b and c are impossible because a square is a rectangle and a rectangle is a parallelogram.

Field-Test Comments

We used this activity with four sixth-grade classes the day before Thanksgiving break. Before distributing the activity, we presented the students with a mini-lesson on quadrilaterals. We would suggest using this comic strip as a culminating project to a quadrilateral unit. The students completed the activity as an independent, in-class assignment. Many of the students enjoyed this hands-on experiment using geoboards. Most students were completely captivated throughout the lesson.

The student work showed several interesting things. (1) Although most of the students indicated that item b was impossible because a square is a rectangle, almost none of them answered item c correctly. That is, they did not understand that a rectangle is also a parallelogram. (2) Many of the students answered item e by creating a trapezoid that was not isosceles. It seems that for trapezoids, they are still operating at a "looks like" van Hiele level rather than thinking about the properties of a trapezoid.

Stephanie Saviola
Cattaraugus–Little Valley Middle School
Cattaraugus, New York
and
Sue McMillen
Buffalo State College
Buffalo, New York

My advanced fifth graders study seventh- and eighth-grade mathematics. I used this activity as a pre-assessment before our geometry unit. We briefly discussed the cartoon and the first question. The students then answered question 1 individually. They worked in pairs with geoboards to answer question 2. Almost all the students correctly determined that parts b and c were impossible. However, many students answered question d incorrectly, drawing either a trapezoid or a hexagon. As I teach the unit, we will revisit this activity and further discuss the definition of a parallelogram. The students also need further discussion on the cartoon itself to connect their work on the geoboards with the idea in the cartoon. Overall, the students enjoyed the hands-on approach to comparing polygons, and I think it was an excellent pre-assessment before the geometry unit.

Ellen Horlick
Wyngate Elementary School
Bethesda, Maryland

Other Ideas

- Have students create real-life statements similar to the one Knute makes in the second panel of the cartoon. One example is "Every basketball is a sphere, but not every sphere is a basketball."
- Students might enjoy using an electronic geoboard such as the one on NCTM's Web site at http://standards.nctm.org/document/eexamples/chap4/4.2/index.htm.

Adapted from "Cartoon Corner," *Mathematics Teaching in the Middle School,* February 2005, page 388,
edited by Sue McMillen

Under Cover

Luann *by Greg Evans*

Luann, by Greg Evans, 8/19/97. © GEC Inc./Dist. By United Feature Syndicate, Inc.

1. How did the paint clerk arrive at the 44? Draw a top-down sketch of the perimeter of Luann's room to show this number. Use the scale 1/4 inch = 1 foot.

2. Use the answer of 1.28 gallons to determine the allotment for the window and the door. How did you arrive at your answer?

3. If the paint Luann wants to buy costs $19.99 a gallon, and comes only in 1-gallon cans, how much would she spend to paint her room? Add sales tax of 7 percent.

4. As a fraction, about how much of a gallon of paint is left over? What would you suggest Luann do with the leftover paint?

Solutions

(Teacher note: Be aware that the word *allotment* in the cartoon and in problem 2 will trip up some students, and discuss it beforehand. Also, the humor is subtle, and some students won't understand it—a prior discussion is recommended.)

1. The top-down sketch should help students visualize that the perimeter of a 10-foot-by-12-foot room is 44 feet.
2. Calculate that 1.28 gallons of paint would cover (1.28 gallons) × (250 square feet per gallon), or 320 square feet of wall. A perimeter of 44 feet times a wall height of 8 feet results in 352 square feet. So 352 - 320, or 32 square feet, was subtracted from 352 as the allotment for a window and a door.
3. Luann would need 2 gallons at \$19.99 per gallon, or \$39.98 for the paint: \$39.98 × 1.07 = \$42.78 for the cost including tax.
4. About 3/4 of a gallon would remain. The hope is that students would see that 0.28 gallons is close to 0.25 gallons, and recognize that number as the benchmark fraction 1/4. Luann might paint some furniture in her room to match the walls, or save the leftover paint for touch-up work. Mention that Luann should not pour out the leftover paint—many communities have hazardous waste pick-up days for removal of such materials.

Field-Test Comments

This cartoon was used in an average eighth-grade class in mid-December as a review of a chapter we had just completed. Students didn't see the humor right away and stumbled over the word *allotment*. Once we discussed those items, they got back on track and enjoyed the activity. They were successful with problem 3 in particular, and I received some interesting suggestions for problem 4—paint the adjoining bathroom, paint a smaller room, or use it to splash the walls of another room as a decorative application.

Jeanne C. Gagliardo
Safety Harbor Middle School
Safety Harbor, Florida

Other Ideas

- Have students go through a similar problem but for their own bedroom or the mathematics classroom. In particular, the top-down drawing should help develop spatial sense if they sketch where the furniture is. Students might also have more items to remove from the area of the walls than just one window and one door.
- NCTM's Illuminations site has a series of four lessons on designing and building a clubhouse. See http://illuminations.nctm.org/LessonDetail.aspx?id=U172.

Adapted from "Cartoon Corner," *Mathematics Teaching in the Middle School,* March–April 1998, page 434, edited by Julie Fisher

What's in a Name?

Little Dillon Is Smart Guy *by Christopher Dow and Susan Skaar*

1. Rewrite the directions on the math test above to require mathematical answers as the names.
   Directions:

2. Take the “new test” that requires mathematical answers, and name the four figures.

   Figure 1: ______________ Figure 2: ______________

   Figure 3: ______________ Figure 4: ______________

3. List as many geometry terms as possible that apply to each figure above.

Figure Number	Terms That Apply:
1	
2	
3	
4	

Solutions

1. The directions might say to "give mathematical names" or "use geometry terms" to name polygons.
2. The most specific names would be *right triangle, trapezoid, parallelogram,* and *octagon.* Students might give other correct names. (The "right triangle" doesn't have the proper notation for a right angle, but most students will give this name anyway.)
3. Answers will vary. Expect students to write such terms as the following:
   Figure 1: right angle; isosceles; two sides perpendicular; two acute angles; and so forth
   Figure 2: two sides parallel; two congruent, acute angles; two congruent, obtuse angles; polygon; quadrilateral; and so forth
   Figure 3: parallelogram; two sets of parallel sides; two sets of congruent sides; polygon; quadrilateral; and so forth

Field-Test Comments

I used this cartoon with my eighth-grade students on an afternoon between units as a review of polygons and the mathematical terms associated with describing them. They remembered learning about polygons in sixth grade and a little in seventh grade. I wrote *polygon* on the board and had them write what they knew about them on an index cards quietly for 4–5 minutes. Then I had them in groups of four discuss what they wrote down and create a larger, group list. I walked around listening to the groups, then summarized key terms (*closed, regular/irregular, sides, angles,* etc.) I showed them the cartoon on the overhead, hoping they could see the lettering better. They "got" the joke, thought it was lame, but clearly got the point. I talked about how teachers write directions thinking they are clear, but can often be unclear either because of how the directions are written or because the students don't read them well. Then I gave them the activity sheet. They worked on the activities in pairs.

They liked rewriting the directions, but many of them were very unclear about how to improve on them. They wrote things like "apply mathematical terms to each polygon." I had to redirect them to be more specific. Problem 2 was very easy. Problem 3 was a good use of the previous brainstorm of ideas about polygons.

This activity would be a good introduction to a unit on identifying polygons in sixth and seventh grades, or as a quick review for subsequent years, especially for eighth graders who study algebra and start to "forget" geometry.

Glenn Kenyon
San Francisco School
San Francisco, California

Other Ideas

- Students who need extra work on this topic would enjoy the activity "Roping In Quadrilaterals" in *Navigating through Geometry in Grades 3–5* from NCTM. A CD-ROM that accompanies the book has an enjoyable applet called Shape Sorter that some students would particularly enjoy.
- For more practice with identifying polygons, students will enjoy the game Polygon Capture found at http://illuminations.nctm.org/LessonDetail.aspx?id=L270.

Adapted from "Cartoon Corner," *Mathematics Teaching in the Middle School,* September–October 1996, page 30, edited by Ann Lawrence

5

Holidays

Burgers and Birds

Place your answers on the back of this sheet.

1. The customer buys a half a pound of hamburger meat on Monday, three-fourths of a pound on Tuesday, and one pound on Wednesday. If this pattern continues to grow for a week, how many quarter-pound hamburgers will she be able to make from the hamburger meat that was purchased over the seven-day period?

11-27 © Jim Unger/dist. by United Media, 1997

HERMAN®

"I'm giving thanks for hamburger. Give me half a pound."

Herman, by Jim Unger, 11-27-97 HERMAN® is reprinted with permission
from LaughingStock Licensing Inc., Ottawa, Canada. All Rights Reserved.

2. A shopping cart can hold up to 125 pounds, and the turkeys hanging over the meat cutter's head weigh an average of 18.5 pounds each. Would the customer be able to purchase and carry out all seven turkeys at the same time in her shopping cart? Explain your answer.

3. In 2004, about 264 million turkeys were raised worldwide. Write this number in scientific notation. If 46 million of those turkeys were eaten at Thanksgiving, what percent of turkeys raised were eaten on this traditional American holiday? (Round your answer to the nearest whole percent.)

4. According to a survey commissioned by the National Turkey Federation, the top five ways consumers eat leftover turkey are shown in the chart. Construct a circle graph that shows these data. Write three questions (with complete solutions) that could be answered using your graph.

Leftovers Eaten As	Percent
Sandwich	48
Soup or stew	20
Salad	14
Casserole	12
Stir-fry	6

Solutions

1. She can make $0.5 + 0.75 + 1.00 + 1.25 + 1.50 + 1.75 + 2.00 = 8.75$; $8.75 \div 0.25 = 35$ quarter-pounders.
2. The customer would not be able to carry out all seven turkeys, because they weigh a total of 129.5 pounds and the shopping cart holds only 125 pounds. Students might be encouraged to solve $A = t/n$ algebraically for t, with A being the average of 18.5, n being the number of turkeys (7), and t being the total weight.
3. In scientific notation, 264 million $= 2.64 \times 10^8$; $46/264 = 0.1742...$, or 17 percent.
4.

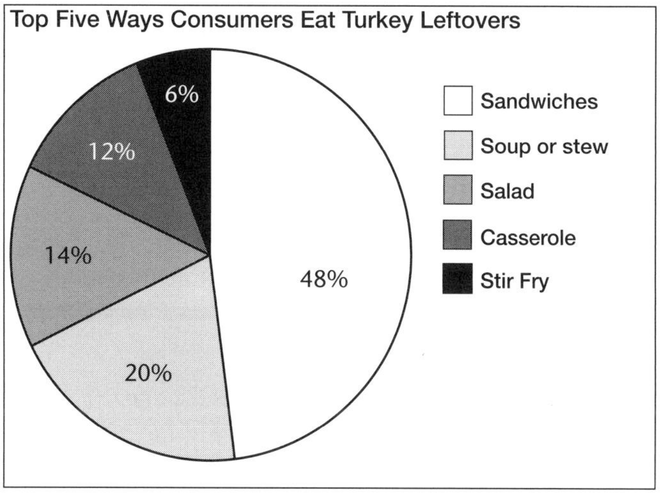

Field-Test Comments

My sixth-grade class worked with this cartoon on the day of our holiday program when our regular schedule was put on hold for a day. This was a good time for the activity because the students were in a relaxed frame of mind and were able to focus on the questions. My students were pretty adept at solving the computation problems. The only thing that gave them trouble was adding the fractions in the first problem. The solutions were all "correct" based on the amount of meat they computed. The class quickly figured out the steps needed for solving questions 2 and 3. Creating the pie chart for question 4 was more challenging, since they did it free-hand. I suggested they try dividing up the pie like a chart to begin with. In the end most of the graphs were pretty accurate. The sections were all appropriately sized.

Extension questions that could be asked are, Will the lady be eating alone? What do you think her dinner menu might be? Explain your thinking.

Tom Lewis
Hamilton Elementary School
Moline, Illinois

Other Ideas

- To make the circle graph in problem 4, students might use technology, such as the applet from NCTM's Illuminations Web site at http://illuminations.nctm.org/ActivityDetail.aspx?ID=60.
- Recreate the first Thanksgiving meal, and have students plan a menu, decide how many people will attend, look up recipes, and adjust for the number of people.

Adapted from "Cartoon Corner," *Mathematics Teaching in the Middle School,* November 2006, page 198, edited by Andy Reeves and Mary Lou Beasley

Perfect Pumpkins

MEG **BY GREG CURFMAN**

1. Sal has 210 pumpkins, and every second pumpkin is *either* too big or too small. How many pumpkins are either too big or small?

2. Every third pumpkin is too oblong. How many pumpkins are too oblong?

3. Every fifth pumpkin is too flat. How many pumpkins are *both* too oblong and too flat?

4. How many pumpkins are too big or too small, too oblong, and also too flat?

5. Use the Venn diagram to help organize your thoughts. The circles represent pumpkins that are too big or too small, too oblong, and too flat.

   a) The center section is for pumpkins with three imperfections. Place the answer to question 4 in the center of the diagram.

   b) The remaining sections of the diagram are for the number of pumpkins with one or more imperfections. Complete the diagram by writing the correct number in each section. Some, but not all, of the numbers can be found in problems 1–3.

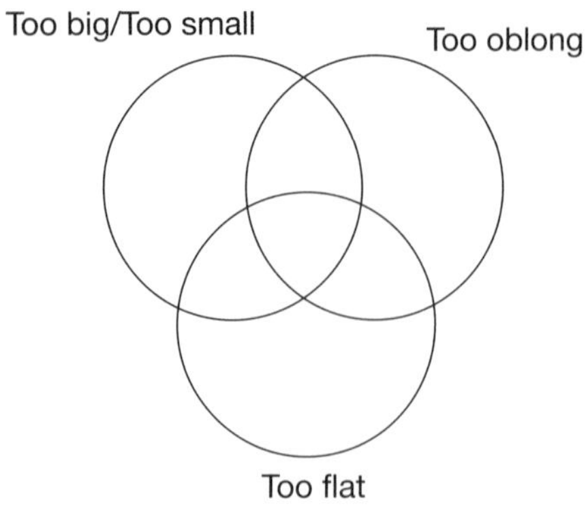

6. How many perfect pumpkins are in Sal's pumpkin patch?

Solutions

1. Calculating 210/2 gives 105 pumpkins that are too big or too small.
2. Calculating 210/3 gives 70 pumpkins that are too oblong.
3. If every fifth pumpkin is too flat and every third pumpkin is too oblong, then every fifteenth pumpkin is both too flat and too oblong; 210/15 = 14 pumpkins are both too flat and too oblong.
4. If every second pumpkin is too big or too small, every third pumpkin is too oblong, and every fifth is too flat, then every thirtieth pumpkin has all three imperfections. So 210/30 = 7 pumpkins have three imperfections.
5. The Venn diagram shows 154 **imperfect** pumpkins.

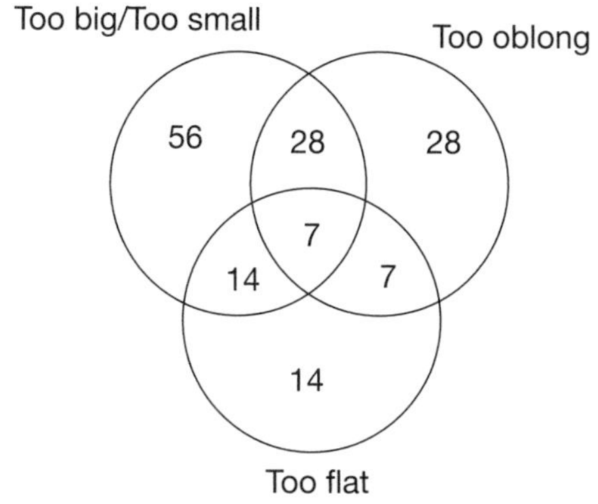

6. Subtracting 154 from 210 gives 56 pumpkins that are perfect.

Field-Test Comments

My 8th-grade regular class used this cartoon in October to align with the Halloween theme. Questions 3 and 4 challenged them, but they rose to the occasion upon whole class discussion of ways to use the LCM. They worked with partners to complete the Venn diagram, which some students found confusing. Again, a class discussion and whole-group work cleared up the difficulties, and they completed the diagram accurately. I would recommend reviewing triple Venn diagrams using student characteristics—eye color, hair color, glasses or no glasses, for example—and LCM before using the cartoon.

Barbara Brown
Clearwater Intermediate School
Clearwater, Florida

Other Ideas

- Have students formulate problems about Sal's discount policy. Ex: Sal agrees to sell all the pumpkins in his patch. Perfect pumpkins are \$5.00 each. Pumpkins that are too big or small are reduced 10 percent. Pumpkins that are too oblong are reduced 20 percent. Pumpkins that are too flat are reduced 30 percent. Pumpkins with more than one defect get more than one discount. A pumpkin that is too small and too flat gets a 10 percent discount plus a 30 percent discount, for a total discount of 40 percent. What is the total value of the pumpkins in Sal's pumpkin patch? (\$864.50)

Adapted from "Cartoon Corner," *Mathematics Teaching in the Middle School,* October 2000, page 110, prepared by Eric Golombek; edited by Judith A. White

Santa's Performance

CLOSE TO HOME **BY JOHN McPHERSON**

1. If Santa's performance continued to decrease 5 percent each year, what percent of the toys did he deliver in 1999? In 2000? In 2001?

Year	1997	1998	1999	2000	2001
Percent	32	27			

2. Use the graph to plot Santa's performance for 1997 through 2001. Connect the points with a dotted line, and continue the dotted line to estimate Santa's performance for 2002 _____ and 2003______.

3. Why is a dotted line used in this situation instead of a solid line?

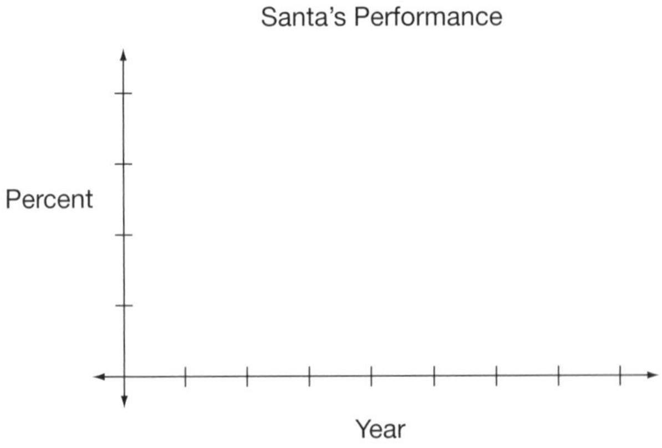

4. Extend the line on your graph to determine in what year Santa's performance slumped to 0 percent. ________

5. If Santa *increased* his deliveries from 27 percent to 33 percent in 1999, and then to 39 percent in 2000, and this same pattern continued, in what year would his performance first exceed 50 percent?

Solutions

1. He delivered 22 percent in 1999; 17 percent in 2000; 12 percent in 2001.
2. Estimate 7 percent in 2002; 2 percent in 2003. Students' graphs should look like the one below.

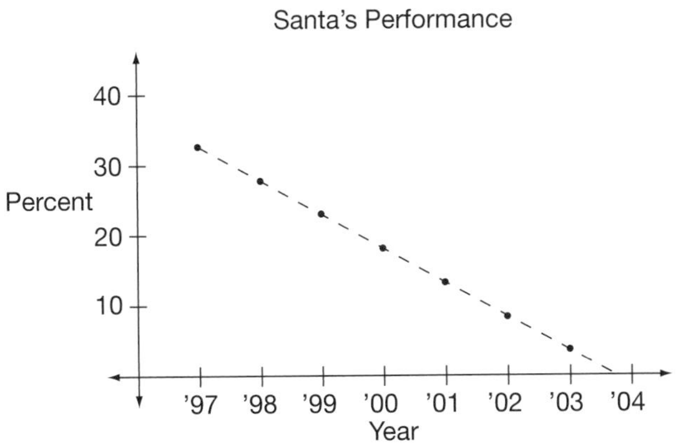

3. A dotted line is called for because the graph represents a discrete set of points rather than a continuous set.
4. Santa's performance will reach 0 percent in 2004.
5. Santa's performance will exceed 50 percent in 2002.

Field-Test Comments

My 8th-grade prealgebra classes completed this activity—the questions were clear and prompted student responses. They had no difficulty with constant rate of change and using a graph to make predictions. Question 3 provided an opportunity to introduce continuous versus discrete data.

Joyce L. Wiley
Osceola Middle School
Seminole, FL

Other Ideas

- As an extension, ask students to extend the graph to other quadrants and interpret the results as they relate to the cartoon. Algebra students could be asked to write an equation for determining Santa's performance from the rate of change and the initial performance, and use the equation to find when Santa's performance was 100 percent.
- See NCTM's *Illuminations* Web site for "Shopping Mall Math": http://illuminations.nctm.org/LessonDetail.aspx?id=U99.
- An Illuminations activity "Walk the Plank" can be found at http://illuminations.nctm.org/LessonDetail.aspx?id=L682. Like this lesson, it also involves a negative slope, which can often be hard to find in a real context, and gets students actively involved physically.

Adapted from "Cartoon Corner," *Mathematics Teaching in the Middle School*, December 2000, page 243, edited by Judith A. White

Trick or Treat?

Fox Trot *by William Amend III*

1. On what day of the year should this cartoon appear in the newspaper? Explain how you know you are correct.

2. Assume no leap year. What holiday falls 5.256×10^5 minutes *after* Halloween?

3. If October starts on the first day of the week, Sunday, then Halloween falls on the third day of the week, Tuesday. Make a table that compares October starting days with Halloween days. If the day of the week October starts on is d, write an algebraic expression that represents on what day of the week Halloween will fall. (Assume that after day 7, the days of the week start over again at day 1.)

Day of Week October Starts On	1 (Sun.)	2 (Mon.)	3 (Tues.)	4 (Wed.)	5 (Thur.)	6 (Fri.)	7 (Sat.)	d
Day of Halloween								?

4. At Justin's Halloween party, the letters in the word HALLOWEEN are written on pieces of paper and placed in a bag. If a player pulls out a certain letter, that person wins a prize. List the probabilities of pulling out each letter as a fraction, a decimal, and a percent.

	P(H)	P(A)	P(L)	P(O)	P(W)	P(E)	P(N)
Fraction							
Decimal							
Percent							

Solutions

(*Teacher note:* Remove the date in the third frame of the cartoon before using it with your class. Also be prepared for the eventuality that some students will not participate because of religious beliefs.)

1. October 17. Calculate $2 \times 10 = 20{,}000$ minutes = $333.\overline{3}$ hours = $13.\overline{8}$ days. Counting backward 13.8 days from October 31 gives October 17.
2. Halloween. Calculate $5.256 \times 10^5 = 525600$ minutes = 8760 hours = 365 days.
3.

Day of Week October Starts On	1 (Sun.)	2 (Mon.)	3 (Tues.)	4 (Wed.)	5 (Thur.)	6 (Fri.)	7 (Sat.)	d
Day of Halloween	3 (Tues.)	4 (Wed.)	5 (Thur.)	6 (Fri.)	7 (Sat.)	1 (Sun.)	2 (Mon.)	$d + 2$

4.

	P(H)	P(A)	P(L)	P(O)	P(W)	P(E)	P(N)
Fraction	1/9	1/9	2/9	1/9	1/9	2/9	1/9
Decimal	$0.\overline{1}$	$0.\overline{1}$	$0.\overline{2}$	$0.\overline{1}$	$0.\overline{1}$	$0.\overline{2}$	$0.\overline{1}$
Percent	≈ 11.1%	≈ 11.1%	≈ 22.2%	≈ 11.1%	≈ 11.1%	≈ 22.2%	≈ 11.1%

Field-Test Comments

This cartoon was used as a warm-up exercise on Halloween Day in three Algebra I honors classes. The students had an individual copy and I had an overhead copy as we discussed the cartoon. Questions 1 and 2 were handled nicely by the students with whole-class discussion. Question 3 was a challenge, as we were no longer doing algebraic expressions. Question 4 was interesting and went smoothly.

Elizabeth Wright
Bay Point Middle School
St. Petersburg, Florida

Other Ideas

- Make up similar questions for a different holiday, and then have students ask them of one another.
- Have students find a mathematics vocabulary term that starts with each letter in Halloween, and either write the definition or draw a picture, or both. (Ex. H = hexagon, ...)
- Have students use a calculator to investigate the pattern in the decimal representations for the ninths, first by writing decimals for 1/9 and 2/9, then conjecturing, and finally verifying, for 3/9, 4/9, 5/9, and so on.

Adapted from "Cartoon Corner," *Mathematics Teaching in the Middle School,* September–October 1995, page 468, edited by Barbara Cain

6

Numbers and Numeration

Cool Beans

Adam *by Brian Bassett*

1. Clayton's dad drinks 4 cups of coffee out of the mug each day. Use a calculator to find how many days he used the mug to reach 975,364 cupfuls? How many years was this?

2. On the basis of your results from question 1, is Clayton's statement reasonable? Justify your answer.

3. The number of coffee beans produced in the world is forecast to rise to 7 million tons annually. Since coffee is usually sold by the pound, how many pounds of coffee would this amount be?

4. **Challenge**
   (a) Estimate the cost of buying and drinking one soda every day for a year.

   (b) Increase the price of the soda by 5 percent each year until you turn 18. What will the soda cost each year?

   (c) Estimate the cost of buying a soda every day from now until you turn 18.

Solutions

(*Teacher note:* Many students will not know what the Smithsonian Institution is. Briefly discuss that this institution, located in Washington, D.C., is a collection of museums and other entities that house some of this country's greatest treasures. Museums they might have heard of are the Air and Space Museum and the National Museum of American History. Also, please have students use a calculator so they do not get overly bogged down with computation.)

1. 243,841 days; about 668 years
2. No. If Clayton's dad used the mug for 10 years, he would need to drink 267 cups of coffee every day, which is not possible.
3. A ton is 2000 pounds, so $7{,}000{,}000 \times 2000 = 14{,}000{,}000{,}000$ pounds. Students might think of how to make that answer more meaningful by comparing it with items whose weights they have a feel for.
4. Answers will vary. If a soda costs $1.00, then a year's worth of sodas would cost $365.00. The second year, you'd pay 105 percent of $365, or $383.25. For the third year, 105 percent of $383.25 is $402.42. For just three years of sodas every day, you would pay a total of $1150.67. Students might want to set up a table to record their data in an organized manner.

Field-Test Comments

We explored this cartoon in October in a seventh-grade basic class. The students had recently studied measurement, so they weren't intimidated by the material. They welcomed the idea of working with a cartoon, although many of them had not heard of the Smithsonian Institution. The questions were straightforward, which was appropriate for this group that contained many English as a Second Language learners.

Mary Jackson
Pinellas Park Middle School
Pinellas Park, Florida

Other Ideas

- Visit the Smithsonian Institution's Web site (http://www.si.edu/) or one for educators (http://www.smithsonianeducation.org/educators/) for some interesting lesson plans involving large numbers.
- Have students calculate their age in months, days, hours, minutes, and seconds and find the largest unit that they can use that makes their age bigger than one million of that unit.
- Students might enjoy using a spreadsheet to do problem 4 so they can easily extend it beyond age 18. (They could also easily set up a solution using a four-function calculator with repeating-function concept and the memory feature.) They might also enjoy choosing some other habit that they do daily or weekly and calculating its cost over their life expectancy after adding on the cost of inflation.

Adapted from "Cartoon Corner," *Mathematics Teaching in the Middle School*, September 2003, page 28, prepared by Mary M. Sullivan; edited by Sue McMillen

Don’t Ride with Loon!

Shoe *by Chris Cassatt and Gary Brookins*

Shoe, by Chris Cassatt and Gary Brookins (8/8/2005) © Tribune Media Services, Inc. All Rights Reserved. Reprinted with permission.

1. What other numbered buses might Loon have taken? How many times would he have taken each one?

2. If Loon had missed bus number 24 instead of bus number 28, what other bus choices would he think he could take?

3. If Loon had missed bus number 23 instead of bus number 28, what other bus choices would he think he could take?

4. The bus numbers from 2 through 31 are listed below. Circle those for which Loon would think he had only one other choice if he missed that bus number. For those you don’t circle, write the other buses he could take.

2 ______	7 ______	12 ______	17 ______	22 ______	27 ______
3 ______	8 ______	13 ______	18 ______	23 ______	28 ______
4 ______	9 ______	14 ______	19 ______	24 ______	29 ______
5 ______	10 ______	15 ______	20 ______	25 ______	30 ______
6 ______	11 ______	16 ______	21 ______	26 ______	31 ______

5. If Loon were put in charge of defining *prime number*, how might he define it? (Hint: What’s the difference in the number of buses Loon thinks he could take, from your list in question 4 above?)

Solutions

1. Loon might have taken bus 2 fourteen times, bus 7 four times, bus 4 seven times, or bus 1 twenty-eight times.
2. Loon would think he could take buses 1, 2, 3, 4, 6, 8, and 12. Each of those buses is a factor of 24, and Loon thinks he could take a bus a certain number of times if the product of the bus number and the number of times he took it equals the bus number.
3. Loon would think that he could take bus 1 twenty-three times. However, 23 has no factors other than 1 and 23 itself, so he wouldn't think of taking another numbered bus.
4. The list would have the prime numbers from 2 through 31 circled: 2, 3, 5, 7, 11, 13, 17, 19, 23, 29, and 31. The other numbers would have the factors listed.
5. Loon would probably make a statement defining prime number as being equivalent to "a bus number for which you could substitute only one other bus for it, bus 1."

Field-Test Comments

I used this cartoon with sixth-grade students in a dropout-prevention program. I picked a small group of six students at a time and worked with them using the overhead. Some got it immediately, and the rest got it with a few clues and some scaffolding on my part. Most of the students found it to be entertaining and humorous!

Greg Fanning
Lealman Intermediate School
St. Petersburg, Florida

Other Ideas

- Supporting lessons, games, and activities on prime and composite numbers can be found at NCTM's Illuminations Web site. Consider these options: http://illuminations.nctm.org/ActivityDetail.aspx?ID=12, http://illuminations.nctm.org/ActivityDetail.aspx?ID=29, and http://illuminations.nctm.org/ActivityDetail.aspx?ID=64.
- Students might enjoy this problem: "Write each even number greater than 2 but less than 32 as the sum of two prime numbers." The problem is an introduction to Goldbach's conjecture, one of the most famous unsolved problems in mathematics: Every even number greater than 2 is the sum of two prime numbers.

Adapted from "Cartoon Corner," *Mathematics Teaching in the Middle School,* May 2006, page 446,
edited by Andy Reeves and Mary Lou Beasley

How High Are the Stars?

Baby Blues *by Rick Kirkman and Jerry Scott*

Baby Blues, by Rick Kirkman and Jerry Scott, 9/6/99. © Baby Blues Partnership, King Features Syndicate. Used with permission. All Rights Reserved.

1. The Sun is about 9.3×10^7 miles from Earth. Light travels at a speed of 1.86×10^5 miles per second. How long does it take light from the Sun to reach Earth?

2. It takes light from the Moon 1¼ seconds to reach Earth. What is the distance between Earth and the Moon?

3. Astronomers use the astronomical unit (AU) to measure relative distances between planets. One astronomical unit is about 93,000,000 miles, the distance between Earth and the Sun. Use the table to find the distance in miles between Jupiter and Saturn.

Planet	Distance from Planet to Sun in Astronomical Units
Mercury	0.39
Venus	0.72
Earth	1.00
Mars	1.52
Jupiter	5.2
Saturn	9.52

4. Uranus is approximately twice as far from the Sun as Saturn. What is the approximate distance between Uranus and the Sun?

Solutions

1. About 500 seconds, or approximately 8.3 minutes
2. Approximately 2.3×10^5 miles
3. About 4×10^8 miles
4. About 1.8×10^9 miles

Field-Test Comments

I used this cartoon in December in my advanced sixth-grade mathematics class and my sixth-grade prealgebra class. We were reviewing for both mathematics and science exams because I teach both subjects to the students. The topics taught during this semester that were covered in this cartoon were scientific notation, writing equations, multiplying and dividing decimals, problem solving, and the formula for speed. This was also a nice introduction to the use of cartoons, which I usually begin to use in January. I make overheads of the cartoons and use them as bell work, finding ones that relate to the topics we are studying or have studied.

The cartoon captured their interest, and I directed my advanced class through each question. The topic of space and distance fascinated them, and they were eager to complete the questions. Once they understood how to solve questions 1 and 3, questions 2 and 4 became easier. With my prealgebra class, I let students work in small groups to solve the problems. The majority of the students were able to complete the first two questions easily. When they were solving questions 3 and 4, they needed to be reminded to find distance and not just AU. The students found Bode's law—see "Other Ideas"—quite interesting.

Lynn Prichard
Williams International Baccalaureate Middle Magnet School
Tampa, Florida

Other Ideas

- Visit the NCTM Illuminations Web site to investigate activities on distance and number sense. Try http://illuminations.nctm.org/LessonDetail.aspx?id=L25 for a distance activity.
- Visit PBS Teacher Source at http://www.pbs.org/wgbh/aso/resources/guide/phyact4index.html to see an activity in which students can create scale models of Earth, the Moon, and distances in space.
- Students might be interested in Bode's law (sometimes called Titius-Bode law), which predicts the mean distance of the seven inner planets from the Sun. Start with the sequence {0, 3, 6, 12, 24, 48, 96, 192, 384, 768, ...}, in which you double a term (after the first two) to get the next term. Add 4 to each term, and divide by 10. The resulting set of numbers {0.4, 0.7, 1.0, 1.6, 2.8, 5.2, 10.0, 19.6, 38.8} is a close approximation to the mean distance of the planets from the Sun. This set of numbers allowed astronomers to predict another planet between Mars and Jupiter, and suggested where they might look for Neptune and Pluto. They didn't find a planet between Mars and Jupiter, but they did find the asteroid belt.

Adapted from "Cartoon Corner," *Mathematics Teaching in the Middle School,* May 2004, page 489, edited by Sue McMillen

Prime Guess

Adam *by Brian Bassett*

1. How many counting numbers occur between 1 and 100?

2. What is the probability that Katy will randomly pick 23?

3. The number 23 is a prime number. How many prime numbers occur between 1 and 100? Work with a partner—develop a system to find out. Circle the prime numbers below.

1	2	3	4	5	6	7	8	9	10
11	12	13	14	15	161	17	18	19	20
21	22	23	24	25	26	27	28	29	30
31	32	33	34	35	36	37	38	39	40
41	42	43	44	45	46	47	48	49	50
51	52	53	54	55	56	57	58	59	60
61	62	63	64	65	66	67	68	69	70
71	72	73	74	75	76	77	78	79	80
81	82	83	84	85	86	87	88	89	90
91	92	93	94	95	96	97	98	99	100

4. **Challenge**
   (a) Start with any number from the chart above. **Add** 6. **Multiply** by 2. **Subtract** 8. **Divide** by 2. **Subtract** your "start number." **Multiply** by 12. **Subtract** 1. What is your answer?

   (b) Use algebraic thinking to show why the number trick works with any starting number n. Show your work on the back of this paper.

Solutions

(*Teacher note:* Over time, students will not recognize 23 as basketball legend Michael Jordan's jersey number. You might use that fact as an entry point into the cartoon's humor.)

1. Since 1 and 100 are not included, ninety-eight counting numbers occur. If you have advanced students, you might ask them how many fractions occur between 1 and 100—an infinite number—so the assumption people make is that the problem involves counting numbers.
2. 1/98, again assuming that you are talking about the counting numbers.
3. Twenty-five primes occur between 1 and 100: 2, 3, 5, 7, 11, 13, 17, 19, 23, 29, 31, 37, 41, 43, 47, 53, 59, 61, 67, 71, 73, 79, 83, 89, and 97. Students might develop a system such as this: Circle 2 and then mark out every second number—you've marked out multiples of 2. Circle 3 and then mark out every third number that's not already marked out—you've marked out multiples of 3. They should continue in this fashion until they have circled primes less than the square root of 100 and marked out their multiples.
4. The answer will always be 23, no matter what number is chosen to begin. The steps are shown below. This number trick could be shown at a concrete level with cups representing n and beans representing 1's.

Choose a number n between 1 and 100.	n
Add 6	$n + 6$
Multiply by 2	$2(n + 6) = 2n + 12$
Subtract 8	$2n + 4$
Divide by 2	$n + 2$
Subtract the chosen number (n)	2
Multiply by 12	24
Subtract 1	23

Field-Test Comments

I used this cartoon with my average sixth-grade class in November. We had studied prime numbers but not probability, but they seemed to understand question 2 regardless, probably due to past experience with the topic.

Most of the students liked searching for prime numbers in question 3, and some came up with unusual methods. Question 4 was a challenge that some students were up to—a class of advanced students would probably enjoy the "different flavor" that this problem assumes.

Mary Jackson
Pinellas Park Middle School
Pinellas Park, Florida

Other Ideas

- Have students write their own number tricks and share them with other students.
    - Explain the steps algebraically using the variable n, or cups and beans.
    - Make the answer the starting number.
    - Make the answer 1, or make the answer a prime number other than 23.

Adapted from "Cartoon Corner," *Mathematics Teaching in the Middle School,* January 2000, page 299, edited by Judith A. White

So Many Stars

1. What is the number 3,456,329,592,641 expressed in words?

2. Write the number 3,456,329,592,641 in scientific notation.

3. Round 3,456,329,592,641 to the nearest one hundred billion, and then put the rounded number in scientific notation. For which numbers does scientific notation seem to be more useful? Explain your answer.

"I count 3,456,329,592,641 on my side. How many on yours?"

4. Solve the problems below, and put your answers in scientific notation.

   a. $(3 \times 10^2) \times (3 \times 10^4) =$

   b. $(1.5 \times 10^4) \times (6.1 \times 10^3) =$

   c. $(4.7 \times 10^3) \times (2.0 \times 10^2) =$

   d. $(4.0 \times 10^4) \times (2.1 \times 10^6) =$

   e. $(1.2 \times 10^5) \times (1.1 \times 10^3) =$

   f. $(7.9 \times 10^2) \times (1 \times 10^7) =$

5. Find and state a pattern that gives the product of two numbers in scientific notation without changing the numbers into standard form.

6. **Challenge** Solve these two problems, and put your answers in scientific notation. You'll have to make some adjustment to the product to get the final answer in scientific notation.

   a. $(9 \times 10^4) \times (6 \times 10^3) =$

   b. $(5.0 \times 10^4) \times (8.1 \times 10^6) =$

Solutions

1. Three trillion four hundred fifty six billion three hundred twenty nine million five hundred ninety two thousand six hundred forty one
2. $3.456329592641 \times 10^{12}$
3. 3,500,000,000,000; 3.5×10^{12}. Scientific notation is more useful for numbers that have been rounded and have several consecutive zeros. Otherwise the result is a number with a lot of digits after the decimal place, which looks even more complicated.
4. a. 9×10^6 b. 9.15×10^7 c. 9.4×10^5 d. 8.4×10^{10} e. 1.32×10^8 f. 7.9×10^9
5. Multiply the numbers in front of the powers of 10. Add the exponents to get the new exponent for 10. This tactic works if the product of the leading digits is less than 10; if not, you must adjust the leading number and power of 10, as in the challenge problem.
6. a. 5.4×10^8 b. 4.05×10^{11}

Field-Test Comments

We used this assignment with an advanced seventh-grade mathematics class that had previously been introduced to scientific notation. The students had time to practice putting large numbers into scientific notation and changing them into standard form. The students worked on the questions individually and then discussed their answers with their partners. Overall, it was a great way to get the students thinking about scientific notation and providing a connection to the real world.

Harmonie Conte and Kristen Lasker
Buffalo Public School #89—Dr. Lydia T. Wright School of Excellence
Buffalo, New York
and
Sue McMillen
Buffalo State College
Buffalo, New York

I used this cartoon as an in-class activity with my advanced eighth-grade mathematics class as part of our unit on exponential relationships. The day before, as part of their homework, they got an answer on the calculator that needed to be written in scientific notation, and they needed a little refresher on how to do this. The cartoon worked great to give them a short refresher on how to use scientific notation. My students particularly liked trying to find the patterns for question 5. As we had done the properties of exponents two weeks ago, this question was a great tie-in to those.

Kevin Dykema
Mattawan Middle School
Mattawan, Michigan

Other Ideas

- Ask students in what other fields of study scientific notation might be useful.
- Ask students if their multiplication rule works when multiplying three or more numbers in scientific notation.
- Challenge students to find a rule for dividing two numbers that are written in scientific notation.

Adapted from "Cartoon Corner," *Mathematics Teaching in the Middle School,* November 2003, page 159, edited by Sue McMillen

Which Way Is Forward?

Beetle Bailey

Beetle Bailey, by Mort Walker, 8/1/03. © King Features Syndicate. Used with permission. All Rights Reserved.

A palindrome is a word or number that reads the same forward and backward. The word OTTO and the numeral 737 are examples.

1. Make a list of words that are palindromes.

2. How many 4-digit palindromes are there? Explain how you found your answer. Note: Do not count numbers with a leading zero, since they are written as 3-digit numerals. For example, 0770 is written as 770.

3. The odometer on Jorge's school bus reads 35,953. How many miles will the bus travel before the mileage reading shows the next largest palindrome?

4. Find a 2-digit number that will take more than 3 additions to result in a palindrome. (The example at the right takes 3 additions to create a palindrome from a 2-digit number.)

> *First Addition*
> Start with a 2-digit number: 68
> Reverse the digits and add: 86 + 68 = 154
> *Second Addition*
> Continue to reverse the digits: 154; 451
> Add until a palindrome results: 154 + 451 = 605
> *Third Addition*
> 605 + 506 = 1111

Solutions

1. Answers will vary.
2. Ninety 4-digit palindromes are possible. Ten possibilities occur for the middle two digits—00, 11, 22, 33, 44, 55, 66, 77, 88, and 99. Nine possibilities occur for the first and last digits—the digits 1 through 9. So 10×9, or ninety, different 4-digit palindromes exist. (*Teacher note:* Many students will solve this problem by making a list of the palindromes.)
3. 110 miles
4. 69, 78, 79, 87, 89, 96, 97, 98

Field-Test Comments

We used this activity with two of our sixth-grade Academic Intervention Services classes in early November. A week prior, we introduced the topic of a palindrome in mathematics. For question 1, we worked together, and then the students completed the rest of the activity as an independent, in-class assignment. Our students who normally do not enjoy this class were completely engaged and definitely found it elevating.

For example, one young man who "never does anything" in class, when he found out there were multiple answers to question 4, wanted to keep working until he found them all. Looking through the student sheets showed that most of the students worked diligently at question 4, with several even using additional sheets of paper. This question was a great opportunity for practicing addition. We think it is a good example of allowing students to practice "basic skills" in a richer problem-solving setting.

Stephanie Saviola
Cattaraugus-Little Valley Middle School
Cattaraugus, New York
and
Sue McMillen
Buffalo State College
Buffalo, New York

Other Ideas

- Students can figure out what the previous palindrome was on Jorge's speedometer.
- Students can find a three-digit number that will take more than five additions.
- Students would probably enjoy trying to make a sentence that is a palindrome. Examples:

  Now, Evil, I've won!

  Men, I'm Eminem!

  A Web search will yield many more. A challenge would be to make a palindrome sentence with a numerical palindrome in it.

Adapted from "Cartoon Corner," *Mathematics Teaching in the Middle School*, March 2004, page 374, edited by Sue McMillen

7

Ratio and Proportion

The Aging Process

Frank & Ernest *by Bob Thaves*

Frank and Ernest, by Bob Thaves, 9/97/90. © Thaves/Dist. By Newspaper Enterprise Association, Inc.

1. Why might the mother have aged much faster than her son from his age 13 to age 17?

2. Assume the mother was 24 years old when the boy was born. Assume also that before age 13, the boy and mother aged at the same rate–one year for one year. How old would the mother be when the boy turned 17?

3. Assume the boy's life calmed down and the mother aged only 2 years for each year for the boy, from his age 17 to 21. How old would she be when he turned 21?

4. Assume that after the boy turned 21, the mother and boy returned to a normal relationship and each gained one year while the other was gaining one year. How old was the boy when his mother retired at age 72?

5. Draw a line graph below to show the ages of the mother and her son over the years.

Solutions

1. The humor is that the man was admitting that he had had some "bad years" from age 13 to 17, driving his mother to age prematurely.
2. The mother would be 24 + 13, or 37, when the boy turned 13. Then she aged 20 years while he aged 4 years, so she would be 57 when he turned 17. Students might begin a table to keep up with both ages on this problem, and complete it for problems 3 and 4.
3. The mother would gain 8 years while the son went from 17 to 21, so she would be 57 + 8, or 65.
4. The mother would reach retirement age in 72 – 65, or 7, years. The boy would have gained 7 years during that span also, so he would be 21 + 7, or 28, years old.
5. The graph is shown on the right. Be sure to talk with students about the critical points—where the line begins and where it changes slope—and what the different slopes in the line mean in terms of the rate of change of aging.

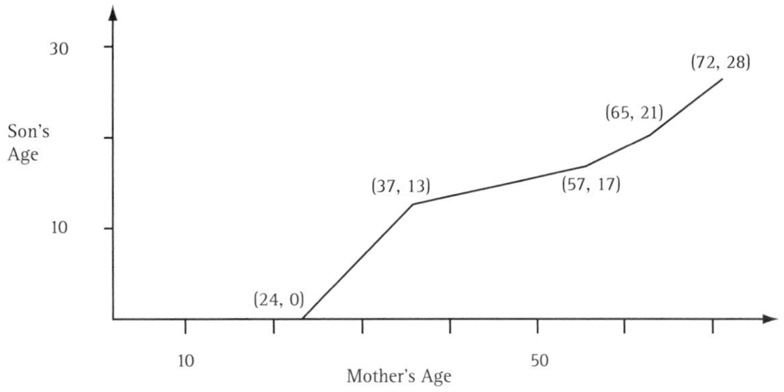

Field-Test Comments

After completing a unit on slope, my eighth-grade Algebra class was given this worksheet while working in small groups. They got quite creative with the first question, trying to outdo one another's hyperbole.

When we finished sharing answers to the questions and going over the graph, I had groups of students calculate the rate of change for each of the segments on the graph. We discussed why the rates changed with the various ages of a teenager. This activity provided an excellent review of the topic, and the students enjoyed the change of pace.

Sue Younker
Spring Wood Middle School
Hanover Park, Illinois

Other Ideas

- Students might have a humorous talk with their parents about this situation, and then draw a similar graph for their own years versus their mother's. They could also create a cartoon and problems similar to the one on the worksheet, and other students could try to match the cartoons with the graphs.
- With advanced students, you might have them determine the slopes of the four line segments that make up the graph.
- Check out more "age problems" at these two sites:
  http://mathforum.org/dr.math/faq/faq.age.problems.html
  http://illuminations.nctm.org/LessonDetail.aspx?id=L668

Adapted from "Cartoon Corner," *Mathematics Teaching in the Middle School,* January 2001, page 307, edited by Judith A. White

Downsizing: An Ancient Art

Hagar the Horrible *by Dik Browne*

Hagar the Horrible, by Dik Browne, 11/4/98. © King Features Syndicate. Used with permission. All Rights Reserved.

Assume the scale on Hagar's map is 1 inch = 200 miles.

1. According to the map, how many inches away is their destination?

2. An ocean is three-and-one-half inches away, on the map, from where they are now. How many miles does this measurement represent?

3. If the men get a map that is half as long and half as wide as this map—but still accurate—how many miles will one inch represent?

4. Measure your bedroom and the major pieces of furniture. Choose a scale so that an accurate drawing of your bedroom will fit on the back of this page or on a sheet of grid paper. Explain below how you know the drawing will fit on the page.

5. **Challenge:** Use the scale from question 4 to draw an accurate map of your bedroom on grid paper or on the back of this sheet. Write your scale on the map.

Solutions

1. 4 inches. Divide 800 miles by 200 miles/inch. Students might also write a proportion, such as 1 inch:200 miles = x inches:800 miles, and solve for x.
2. 700 miles. Multiply $3\frac{1}{2}$ inches × 200 miles/inch. Again, students might write a proportion, such as 1 inch: 200 miles = $3\frac{1}{2}$ inches: x miles, and solve for x.
3. 400 miles. 1 inch will represent twice the length, so 1 inch represents 400 miles.
4. Answers will vary. A group discussion is appropriate, as some students will likely choose metric and others, U. S. customary measures.
5. Answers will vary. You might have a group discussion about problems they ran into making their maps, and how they overcame the problems.

Field-Test Comments

This activity was used in an eighth-grade prealgebra class in October at Southside Fundamental Middle School in St. Petersburg, Florida. The first three problems were not difficult for these students, with proper scaffolding and group interaction, but the last two were somewhat problematic, as they require some initiative. Changes were made to the two problems to make them more accessible to average and below-average students.

Andy Reeves
University of South Florida–St. Petersburg
St. Petersburg, Florida

Other Ideas

- An interesting extension of question 3 would be "What happens to the *area* of a rectangular piece of land when the scale changes as described?" (The area on the map will be $\frac{1}{4}$ of the original map area.) This concept could be extended to doubling or tripling the dimensions.
- Students might enjoy investigating the scales commonly used in making Barbie dolls, model cars, buildings, trains, and so forth.
- An extension into the world of problem solving related to map-making is the famous four-color problem. You can find an easy introduction into the topic on the NCTM's *Figure This! Math Challenges for Families* Web site: http://www.figurethis.org/challenges/c37/challenge.htm.

Adapted from "Cartoon Corner," *Mathematics Teaching in the Middle School,* January–February 1996, page 643, edited by Ann Lawrence

Exercise Exposé

THE FAMILY CIRCUS *by Bil Keane*

"Mommy says to stop counting by fives."

1. If Dad continues counting by fives, will he say "eighty"? "142"? "531"? "2,345"? How can you tell?

2. If Dad has counted to sixty-five, how many push-ups has he really completed? Write an algebraic expression to represent the number of actual push-ups completed if Dad has counted to n.

3. If Dad were counting by 2s instead of by 5s, would he say "eighty"? "142"? "531"? "2,345"? How can you tell?

4. If Dad were counting by 3s instead of by 5s, would he say "eighty"? "142"? "531"? "2,345"? How can you tell?

5. If Dad were counting by 6s instead of by 5s, would he say "eighty"? "142"? "531"? "2,345"? How can you tell?

6. On a recent physical-fitness test, Jason did ten push-ups in forty seconds. "At this rate," Jason stated, "I can do fifteen push-ups in a minute." How accurate is this statement, and how do you know?

7. **Challenge:** Count the number of push-ups you can do in ten seconds. Write a rate statement that describes how many you can do in this time period. How long can you continue at this rate–twenty seconds, one minute, two minutes? What is likely to happen to your rate statement as you get tired?

Solutions

1. He will say "eighty" and "2,345" because both numbers are divisible by 5. He will not say "142" or "531," as they are not divisible by 5. The hope is that students will use divisibility rules as part of their "math talk," saying a number is divisible by 5 if it ends in 0 or 5. This question leads into further divisibility rules in questions 3, 4, and 5.
2. He will have done 13 push-ups, as $65 \div 5 = 13$. The expression that gives Dad's number of push-ups is $n \div 5$.
3. He would say "eighty" and "142," as they are divisible by 2, but would not say "531" or "2,345." Students should say that a number is divisible by 2 if it is an even number or ends in 0, 2, 4, 6, or 8.
4. He would say "531" but not the other numbers. A number is divisible by 3 if the sum of its digits is divisible by 3; the sum of the digits is $5 + 3 + 1$, or 9, and 9 is divisible by 3.
5. He would not say any of the numbers. A number is divisible by 6 if it is divisible by both 2 and 3.
6. If Jason can continue at this rate, his statement is accurate. If Jason does 10 push-ups in 40 seconds, then he would do 5 push-ups in half that time, 20 seconds. So he would do $10 + 5$, or 15, push-ups in $40 + 20$, or 60, seconds, which is 1 minute. Students might use a proportion to solve the problem, or reason that since 60 seconds is $1\frac{1}{2} \times 40$ seconds and since 15 is $1\frac{1}{2} \times 10$ push-ups, the statement is true.
7. Answers will vary, but all students should respond that their rate will decrease as they get tired.

Field-Test Comments

My advanced sixth graders used this cartoon in mid-November. They read the cartoon independently, and then we discussed the main mathematical concepts—divisibility rules and algebra—being used in the activity. They worked in groups to finish the worksheet except for the challenge problem. The students had to consult the divisibility section of their textbook for problem 4, but that was acceptable. Overall, the students were successful on the worksheet and enjoyed it.

Rhody Gecan
Southside Fundamental Middle School
St. Petersburg, Florida

Other Ideas

- Some students might enjoy testing their arm strength using this popular formula:

$$S = (d + p)([w \div 10] + h - 60),$$

where d = dips on a parallel bar, p = pull-ups, w = weight in pounds, and h = height in inches.

- Students might investigate other divisibility rules for 4, 7, and 8 on the Internet.

Adapted from "Cartoon Corner," *Mathematics Teaching in the Middle School,* November–December 1995, page 552, edited by Barbara Cain

2 Bs or 3 Bs

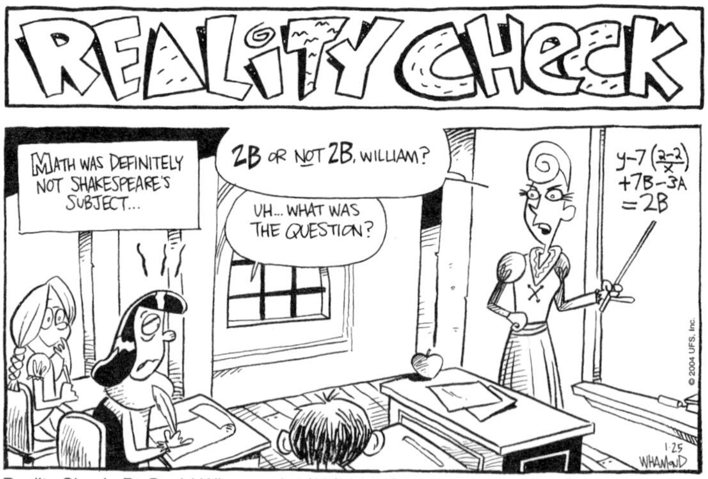

Reality Check, By David Whamond, 1/25/2004. © United Feature Syndicate, Inc.

1. E is the most frequently used letter in the English language. Choose a paragraph in one of your books. What percent of the letters in the paragraph are Es?

2. Samuel Morse, the inventor of Morse code, counted the number of letters in sets of printer type to determine the frequency of letters. He counted 12,000 Es in a set of 105,600 letters. Use a calculator to find the percent of the letters that were Es. How does that value compare with your percent answer from question 1?

3. Morse code represents the letters of the alphabet by short and long sounds. The sounds are then written as dots and dashes. The two simplest codes are one dot or one dash. Which two letters do you think are represented by those codes? Why?

Use the following frequency chart to answer questions 4 and 5. It shows that about 8.167 percent of the letters in typical written English will be the letter A, about 1.492 percent will be Bs, and so on.

A	8.167%	B	1.492%	C	2.782%	D	4.253%	E	12.702%	F	2.228%
G	2.015%	H	6.094%	I	6.996%	J	0.153%	K	0.772%	L	4.025%
M	2.406%	N	6.749%	O	7.507%	P	1.929%	Q	0.095%	R	5.987%
S	6.327%	T	9.056%	U	2.758%	V	0.978%	W	2.360%	X	0.150%
Y	1.974%	Z	0.074%								

4. A page contains 20 Hs. How many I's would you expect on the page? How many Js? How many Gs? Explain how you found your answers.

5. A page contains 20 Hs. Which letter would you would expect to see 30 of? Why?

Solutions

1. Answers will vary.
2. 11.4 percent
3. They are used to represent the two most common letters. One dot represents e, and one dash represents t.
4. The frequency chart used for questions 4 and 5 can be found at http://www.csm.astate.edu/~rossa/datasec/frequency.html.) Note: Answers will vary if a different frequency chart is used. You would expect about twenty-three I's, one J, and seven Gs.

   I: $\frac{20}{6.094} = \frac{x}{6.996}, x \approx 22.96$ J: $\frac{20}{6.094} = \frac{x}{0.153}, x \approx 0.5$ G: $\frac{20}{6.094} = \frac{x}{2.015}, x \approx 6.61$
5. You would expect to find about 30 Ts: $\frac{20}{6.094} = \frac{30}{x}$, so $x = 9.141$, which is very close to 9.056, the expected frequency of T.

Field-Test Comments

I used this activity in my seventh-grade class in mid-November. Students were able to work with a partner and could ask questions of the teacher. Students from all levels–from special education inclusion to honors prealgebra–participated.

The students had one prior experience in converting to percents, as in question 1, several weeks earlier but had not studied percents in depth yet this year. Questions 1 and 2 were the most difficult because the former was new and the big numbers in the latter were intimidating! For question 3, some students drew on their previous knowledge of Morse code, but many got sidetracked by understanding what "dots and dashes" meant even though that was not necessary to answer the question. Students had no experience with proportions, yet were quite comfortable with questions 4 and 5. Although they did not use two equal ratios to solve these problems, they did employ proportional thinking. "These two percentages are close, so the actual numbers must be close, too" was a nice thought that emerged.

This activity would be a nice one to use at the conclusion of a study of percents or proportions.

Susan Eith
Glen Landing Middle School
Blackwood, New Jersey

Other Ideas

- Research and study Morse code. Look for patterns, and make conjectures about why certain characters were coded as they were. Have students create their own codes using only two symbols. Defend why letters/words/phrases were given the code they were given.
- Collect data for question 1 from multiple classes, and compare them. Find the mean, median, and mode. Discuss how larger samples tend to increase accuracy. Test the results with several randomly chosen text passages.
- See "Reinventing Scrabble with Middle School Students" in *Mathematics Teaching in the Middle School* (vol. 5, no. 4 [1999]: 210–13) for a related classroom activity. Students create their own set of Scrabble tiles, choosing both the letter distribution and the point value for each letter. After playing the game with their tiles, the students reflect on their choices and discuss optimal design strategies.
- Consider the similar activity "Amazing Letters" in this book. A related lesson, which involves counting the letters that appear in the names of the fifty states, can be found at NCTM's Illuminations Web site at http://illuminations.nctm.org/LessonDetail.aspx?id=L579.

Adapted from "Cartoon Corner," *Mathematics Teaching in the Middle School,* April 2005, page 404, edited by Sue McMillen

8

Data Analysis and Probability

Amazing Letters

1. How many different two-letter arrangements can you make without repeating letters?

2. How many different three-letter arrangements can you make if you may repeat letters?

3. Write the twenty-six letters of the alphabet on separate pieces of paper, and place them in a box. Draw out four letters, one at a time, and place them in order from left to right below. What is the probability that the letters will spell *math?*

"It's amazing what they can do with only 26 letters!"

4. Write a short paragraph below about you and your friends. Count to determine how many times each letter occurs. What letter occurs most often?

5. Work with the other students to tabulate the results from question 4 for the entire class, and construct a histogram to show the frequency distribution graphically. Calculate the percent of the time that each letter occurs. What letter occurs most often? Use the back of this page for the histogram and for a table of percents by letter.

Solutions

1. You can make 26 × 25, or 650, two-letter arrangements. You have 26 choices for the first letter, and 25 for the second.
2. You can make 26 × 26 × 26, or 17,576, three-letter arrangements. You have 26 choices for all three of the letters.
3. 1/(26 × 25 × 24 × 23), or 1/358,800. Four letters can be pulled at random, without repetition, in 358,800 ways, and only one of those spells *math*.
4. The letter used most often in the English language is *e*. In most samples of 1,000 letters, *e* accounts for approximately 13 percent of the letters.
5. The table below gives the expected distribution of letters for texts of 1000 or more letters.

a	b	c	d	e	f	g	h	i	j	k	l	m
.08	.01	.01	.03	.13	.03	.02	.05	.07	0	0	.02	.03
n	**o**	**p**	**q**	**r**	**s**	**t**	**u**	**v**	**w**	**x**	**y**	**z**
.06	.09	.01	0	.09	.08	.12	.02	0	.01	0	.02	0

Field-Test Comments

My eighth-grade algebra students received this activity as a homework assignment in mid-November. We had studied permutations and combinations earlier, and I wanted to see what they remembered prior to taking the state exam.

The students were really confused by question 3, which led me to reteach the lesson. This type of activity allows a fun way to assess their knowledge before big exams.

Jeanne Gagliardo
Safety Harbor Middle School
Safety Harbor, Florida

Other Ideas

- Consider the related activity "2 Bs or 3 Bs" in chapter 7 of this book. A related lesson, but counting the letters that appear in the names of the fifty states, can be found at NCTM's Illuminations Web site at http://illuminations.nctm.org/LessonDetail.aspx?id=L579.
- Bilingual students or students studying a foreign language might find it interesting to compare the frequency distribution of letters in other languages.
- Not all languages use the twenty-six letters of our alphabet. Only twelve letters of the English alphabet are used for the Hawaiian language. Use a map of Hawaii to make a list of islands and geographic landmarks on the islands. Determine the twelve letters used in their alphabet. Look at the pattern of vowels and consonants.
- A Scrabble game board lists the letter distribution of the ninety-eight game tiles.
  a) Make a scatterplot of the letter-distribution values from question 5 versus the letter-distribution values of the Scrabble tiles. This plot should reveal a positive correlation.
  b) Make a scatterplot of the Scrabble tile letter-distribution values versus the point values of the tiles. This plot should reveal a negative correlation.

Adapted from "Cartoon Corner," *Mathematics Teaching in the Middle School,* April 2000, page 516, edited by Judith A. White

Graphs Alive

1. What kind of graph is pictured in the cartoon?

2. What do the vertical and horizontal axes represent?

3. What is happening in the business to cause the graph line to slope up?

4. What is happening in the business to cause the graph line to slope down?

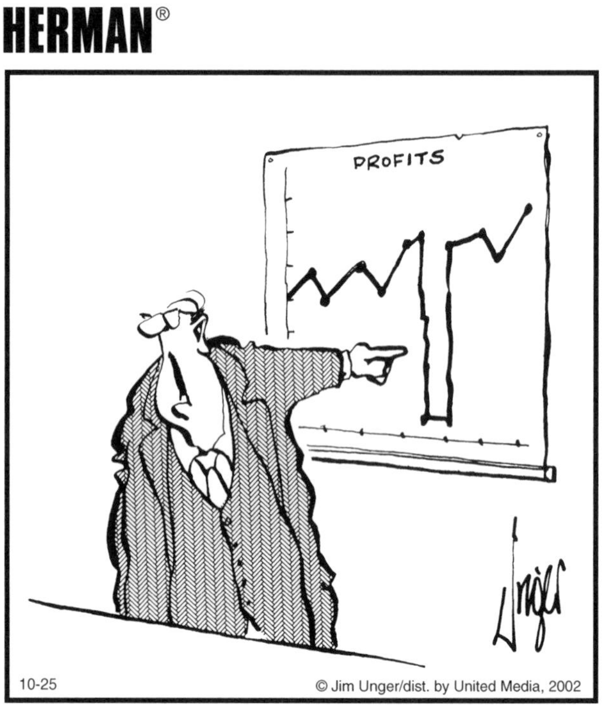

"That's the last time I go on vacation."

Herman, by Jim Unger, 10-20-81. HERMAN® is reprinted with permission from LaughingStock Licensing Inc., Ottawa, Canada. All Rights Reserved.

5. What happened when the cartoon character was on vacation? Why might this situation have occurred?

6. Think of an event in your life that could be shown graphically. (It might be that you were saving for something but had to spend your money suddenly, or the speed of the car/bus as you ride to school in the morning, etc.) At the right, draw a graph of what happened over time. Label both axes appropriately. Notice that you can start the graph below zero!

7. On the back of this page, write a story of the event shown in your graph in question 6. Be sure to explain what happens when the slope of your line changes.

Solutions

1. The graph is a *line graph.*
2. The vertical axis is *profit* (the dependent variable), and the horizontal axis is *time* (the independent variable).
3. When the line slopes up, profits are increasing as time increases. A positive correlation (and a positive slope) exists between the two variables because as one increases, the other also increases. Emphasize the word *slope* as an intuitive introduction to this concept in algebra.
4. When the line slopes down, profits are decreasing as time increases. A negative correlation (and a negative slope) exists between the two variables because as one increases, the other decreases. Again emphasize the word *slope* as an intuitive introduction to this concept in algebra.
5. Graphs will vary. If you share the graphs as a group, you might elect to have students listen to other students' stories and predict what the corresponding graphs will look like or predict the stories from the graphs ahead of hearing them. Also have students talk about things that would make each graph clearer, such as showing units of measure (dollars, minutes, feet, etc.) or labeling the axes or title more clearly. Be sure that students discuss the critical features of each graph, which are points at which the line changes slope.
6. Stories will vary but should match the graphs. Some stories will match their graph more closely than others.

Field-Test Comments

I used this activity with five classes of sixth graders of all ability levels on a "shortened school day." They read the page individually and then were grouped to discuss answers and create the story and line graph. The collaborative groups allowed reluctant students time to become a part of the process. I told them personal line-graph stories of my own to assist in stirring their creative juices.

Most students eventually understood that since line graphs tell a story over time, one of the axes needed to be labeled "time." Even my lowest students made a connection with the meaning of upward and downward slope. Quite a success–I'll use this one again.

Rhody Gecan
Southside Fundamental Middle School
St. Petersburg, Florida

Other Ideas

- *Navigating through Algebra in Grades 6–8* (Reston, Va.: NCTM 2001) has some similar exercises in which students both make graphs for stories, and vice versa.
- The September 1994 issue of *Mathematics Teacher* has some interesting graphs that students would enjoy matching with the respective activities.
- NCTM's Illuminations Web site has some excellent activities related to displaying data graphically. Visit http://illuminations.nctm.org/LessonDetail.aspx?id=U82 and http://illuminations.nctm.org/LessonDetail.aspx?id=U73.

Adapted from "Cartoon Corner," *Mathematics Teaching in the Middle School,* April 1994, page 50, edited by Barbara Cain

Rainman

BORN LOSER® by Art and Chip Sansom

Born Loser, by Art Sansom, 3/28/90. © Newspaper Enterprise Association, Inc.

1. What is the probability of rain on Saturday expressed as a simplified fraction and as a decimal? On Sunday?

2. What is the probability that it will *not* rain on Saturday? On Sunday? On *both* Saturday and Sunday?

3. Use the answer to question 2 to find the probability that it will rain on *either* Saturday or Sunday or both. Was the broadcaster correct?

4. On the back of this sheet, write a statement about yourself and an activity you might do on both Saturday and Sunday independently of each other. Use a mathematically correct conclusion, and then explain your thinking. Below is an example of a statement and a correct conclusion:

> *There is an 80 percent chance that I will talk on the telephone on Saturday, and a 50 percent chance that I will talk on the telephone on Sunday. Therefore, there is a 90 percent chance that I will talk on the telephone this weekend.*

Your statement:

Your conclusion:

Your reasoning:

Solutions

1. On Saturday, the chances are 2/5, or 0.4, and on Sunday they are 3/5, or 0.6.
2. The probability that it will not rain on Saturday is 100 – 40, or 60 percent. The probability that it will not rain on Sunday is 100 – 60, or 40 percent. The probability that it will not rain on both Saturday and Sunday is (60)(40), or 24 percent, since the events are independent. If students have a hard time understanding this concept, have them represent the chances of rain on Saturday with 100 slips of paper of which 40 are marked "rain," and similarly with 100 slips of paper of which 60 are marked "rain" for Sunday. Put the slips in different containers, and randomly pull out 2 slips, one from each container, replacing the slips after each draw. If they draw pairs of slips of paper 100 times, probably neither slip will have "rain" on it approximately 24 draws.
3. If the probability that it will not rain on either Saturday or Sunday is 24 percent, then the chance that it will rain on at least one of those two days, and thus the weekend, is 100 – 24, or 76 percent. This answer can be made more realistic by doing the slips-of-paper activity above and keeping up with how many times students draw "rain" on either one or the other slip of paper, or both. The broadcaster was incorrect.
4. Answers will vary depending on the statements the students write. Their mathematical reasoning is important, and students who have trouble understanding how to make a correct conclusion might be helped by a slips-of-paper activity as described above. In particular, students would be helped by going through the example given prior to attempting this question on their own.

Field-Test Comments

I used "Rainman" as an in-class activity with my eighth-grade mathematics class in December as a way to launch a short unit on probability. As this was at the start of the unit, we didn't discuss how to do questions 3 or 4. They knew the character was wrong in his thinking but didn't know how to calculate the probability. But then near the end of our unit, we came back and discussed those two questions once the students knew how to make tree diagrams.

I found the cartoon to be a good motivator for the students to learn how to make tree diagrams, as they wanted to find the answer to the problem posed.

Kevin Dykema
Mattawan Middle School
Mattawan, Michigan

Other Ideas

- Hamp Sherard, Furman University, describes how to make a tree diagram to determine the probability for problem 3: Make a tree diagram with four paths, three of which have rain on Saturday only or Sunday only, or both days. The sum of these probabilities also gives the probability of rain on the weekend. P(rain on Saturday, rain on Sunday.) + p(rain on Saturday, no rain on Sunday) + p(no rain on Saturday, rain on Sunday) = $(0.4 \times 0.6) + (0.4 \times 0.4) + (0.6 \times 0.6) = 0.24 + 0.16 + 0.36 = 0.76$. Students might enjoy comparing this thinking with the "slips of paper" method.

Adapted from "Cartoon Corner," *Mathematics Teaching in the Middle School,* January–February 1996, page 643, edited by Ann Lawrence

Sorry, Wrong Number!

Born Loser *by Art Sansom and Chip Sansom*

Born Loser, by Art Sansom and Chip Sansom, 10/15/99. © Newspaper Enterprise Association, Inc.

1. Each side of a sheet of paper in a telephone book has four columns with approximately 110 names and numbers in each column. How many two-sided sheets are required to list 1,000,000 telephone numbers? Round the answer to the nearest ten sheets.

2. If neither 0 nor 1 can be used for the first digit of a seven-digit telephone number, how many seven-digit numbers are possible?

3. Guess how many telephone numbers the average person knows. Compare your guess with those of your classmates. Next, you and your classmates should list as many names and telephone numbers as you can remember. What is the total of the phone numbers known for the class? What is the average for the class?

4. **Challenge:** Determine Sam's telephone number using these clues:
   a) Sam's number has seven different digits.
   b) The first digit is twice the second digit.
   c) The average of the first three digits is 6.
   d) The sum of all seven digits is 40.
   e) The product of the seven digits is 60,480.
   f) The last four digits are in the order from least to greatest.

Solutions

1. Calculate $1{,}000{,}000/(2 \times 4 \times 110) = 1136\text{-}4/11$. Approximately 1140 two-sided sheets are needed.
2. Calculate $8 \times 10 \times 10 \times 10 \times 10 \times 10 \times 10$, giving 8,000,000 possible seven-digit numbers.
3. Answers will vary.
4. Sam's telephone number is 846-1579.
   a) The second clue limits the first two digits to 21, 42, 63, or 84.
   b) The third clue limits the first three digits to either 639 or 846. An average of 6 is not possible with the other pairs of numbers.
   c) The fifth clue allows us to do a prime factorization:
   $2 \times 2 \times 2 \times 2 \times 2 \times 2 \times 3 \times 3 \times 3 \times 5 \times 7$
   d) This factorization tells us that 639 cannot be used, because it would require 3 to be used as a factor four times. If the digits 846 are used, the factors $3 \times 3 \times 5 \times 7$ remain.
   e) Clue 1 tells us that all the digits are different, so 3×3 must become 9.
   f) The remaining four digits must be ordered from least to greatest: 1579.

Field-Test Comments

I used this worksheet in mid-November with my regular seventh-grade classes using cooperative groups. We had just finished a problem-solving unit, and this worksheet allowed my students to use some of the skills they had just reviewed. Many student groups jumped right in with drawing a diagram for the first question—they made sketches of what the two pages would look like, and then continued to solve the problem using arithmetic and rounding. The second problem was more difficult, as many of them forgot to include 0 as a choice for digits 3 through 7. They really enjoyed the third question—incorporating anything that they use in real life makes the math more meaningful for my students. The last question was the most fun for many students—they enjoy logic problems, and after solving the one on their worksheet, many of them tried to write their own problems to challenge their classmates and me.

I would make two recommendations to other teachers: first, let the students have ownership by choosing which strategy to use, and second, have the students write their own logic problems using telephone numbers.

Kristin M. Weller
P. K. Yonge Developmental Research School
Gainesville, Florida

Other Ideas

- Have students ask five other people how old they are and how many telephone numbers they have memorized. Construct a data plot to find a possible correlation between age and number of memorized telephone numbers.
- Be careful about students' doing research on telephone numbers. Some Web sites can backtrack from a telephone number to reveal the person's name and quite possibly other information. Students might enjoy a side conversation on the future of telephone books in the era of cell phones.

Adapted from "Cartoon Corner," *Mathematics Teaching in the Middle School,* January 2002, page 293, edited by Judith A. White

Additional Resources from *Mathematics Teaching in the Middle School*

Readers of *Cartoon Corner: Humor-Based Mathematics Activities* may appreciate these other rich collections of problems and their solutions from *Mathematics Teaching in the Middle School:*

- *Menu Collection: Problems Adapted from* **Mathematics Teaching in the Middle School,** compiled and edited by C. Patrick Collier (Reston, Va.: National Council of Teachers of Mathematics and National Middle School Association, 2000). This unique compilation includes more than 225 problems from *Mathematics Teaching in the Middle School,* ranging from "appetizers" (warm-up problems) through "main courses" (more challenging problems) and "desserts" (enrichment problems for students with more problem-solving experience). The problems are conveniently grouped by topic or theme for easy selection.

- *Middle School Mathematics Challenge Poster:* Challenge your students with a poster full of problems designed to stimulate and educate the mind. These middle school level problems can be used in lessons, or placed on the wall in your classroom for students who finish work early. Use the problems as extra credit, or as incentives to earn points for classroom prizes.

Or, add one or more valuable focus issues to your resource shelf:

- *Mathematics Teaching in the Middle School* **Focus Issues.** Offering activities, lesson ideas, teaching strategies, and problems through in-depth articles, departments, and features, this NCTM journal is a great resource for middle school teachers, preservice teachers, and teacher educators. Please see the NCTM online catalog of educational resources at www.nctm.org/catalog for currently available focus issues.

Gain new teaching ideas and engage in ongoing professional development. **Apply for NCTM membership,** including subscription to a **members-only journal** (one of three school-level journals—elementary, middle school, or secondary—or the research journal). For middle school educators, *Mathematics Teaching in the Middle School* addresses the particular learning needs of young adolescent students, the demands these needs place on their teachers, and the issues that capture the vitality of mathematics and characteristics of the middle school student. The journal focuses on investigations that help students develop a strong conceptual understanding of mathematics. Apply quickly and easily at www.nctm.org/membership, or call (800)235-7566.

Please consult www.nctm.org/catalog for the availability of these titles and for a plethora of resources for teachers of mathematics at all grade levels.

❖

For the most up-to-date listing of NCTM resources on topics of interest to mathematics educators, as well as on membership benefits, conferences, and workshops, visit the NCTM Web site at www.nctm.org.